THIRD STAR

Screenplay by Vaughan Sivell

SCREEN SCRIPT

Acknowledgments
Thanks to Franki Goodwin, Tom Betts, Mark Mansfield

First impression: 2014

Published with the financial support of the Welsh Books Council

Editor: Tracy Spottiswoode

Photos: Jamie Stoker

ISBN: 978-0-9929308

Printed on acid free paper. Published by Ffilm Cymru Wales
Ffilm Cymru Wales, S4C Media Centre, Parc Tŷ Glas, Llanishen,
Cardiff CF14 5DU

and printed and bound in Wales by Cambrian Printers,
Llanbadarn Road,
Aberystwyth,
Ceredigion SY23 3TN

I LIKE THE WAY YOU'VE BROUGHT IT BACK AROUND TO YOU DYING, I'D FORGOTTEN

Contents

Foreword by Vaughan Sivell

Third Star was the first film we made at Western Edge Pictures. It was my first time being on a film set where it was my name above the door. I loved it. For all the adventures it led to… There are LOTS more Third Star behind-the-scenes adventures with Tom, Benedict, JJ, Adam and my amazing crew, but there are also many interesting (screenwriter and producer) forays cropping up, as I move on to the next films with my team. It's time to mix in the current with the retrospective. So, just because the DVD is coming out, don't think I'm leaving Barafundle Bay behind.

I love that this part of my career began with Third Star. The film was all heart from the beginning, sitting alone in my study, and continued to be both inspiring and gut wrenching as we trekked through raising the finance, on through production and right through the release. Sure, it was tough at times, but I also had the time of my life and made so many friends I will have forever. That's the real joy of the film business I think.

"My @thisisthirdstar DVD has shipped this morning. All is beautiful."
@linnetdust, Twitter

For those who are keen enough to read the shooting script for Third Star, you'll see there are some scenes in there that didn't make the final cut. In some cases this is a shame, in others I'm so glad they never made it. But here it is warts and all. "The past is a foreign country…" I wrote differently there.

Anyway, I know there are some writers following this who may find that interesting. It's draft 19 which, actually, wasn't the last but it's not too dissimilar from the first... long before Barafundle Bay became Third Star...After getting its premiere as the closing Night Gala film of the Edinburgh International Film Festival in the summer of 2010, Third Star was released theatrically in London and Cardiff on May 20 2011. From that moment the strength of the passionate support that existed from the fans of the film seemed to take over. And we were astounded.

Due to fan demand it was held over at the Empire Leicester Square, then rolled out regionally in the UK and also played at over 40 screens – from NYC to New Orleans – in the USA as part of the "From Britain with Love" programme. In many cases it was booked thanks to the fans who followed us via on Twitter and Facebook who lobbied their local cinemas to show the film.

Third Star is a small film about big ideas. We built it on a lightweight budget, but with ultimate faith in our heavyweight cast. The reward for our belief in the film and for the efforts it took to bring it to the screen was in the unprecedented demand from the ever-faithful fans.

If you were one of them – Thank You. Thank you so much. I can say with all honesty that as a demographic, we soon found out that you are intelligent and actually really... nice. There's no better word for it! We also learned quickly that you're really knowledgeable about all the things we really like too...

We have been inspired by you – and releasing Third Star has lead us to develop a slate of projects we believe you will love, and also to find ways that you can be involved from as EARLY in the process as possible in making those films and bringing them to you.

We loved having you around – and we hope you will all come with us on our next adventures.

Interview with Vaughan Sivell

Tom Betts interviewed Vaughan Sivell about Third Star in Cardiff on Wednesday 25th September 2013. The transcript is below, edited and condensed for your reading pleasure.

What was the first screenplay you ever read?

I think it was the scripts to Blackadder, actually. They were not film screenplays but those were the first scripts I ever read.

So that was the first thing you ever saw with Interior, Exterior ...

Yeah, exactly. I was going to go into writing comedy and all of a sudden I got lots of books of scripts so it was that, Monty Python, Frasier, Cheers, Seinfeld.

Were you picking them apart, trying to work out the different elements?

I was. I think that despite not having a maths brain, there is a maths problem in all scripts: how do you get into a thing, what do we know, how quickly do we know it, and how do you get out of it? I always say to anyone that writing sketch comedy is the best training for writing film scripts because they're really hard to end. You have to get in, say an awful lot, deliver some punchlines and get out satisfactorily. And of course that's what you have to do with every scene in a film. I got into writing sketch comedy with a partner and we became obsessed with (as most comedy writers seem to) writing the perfect sketch. They're like haikus for a poet, I guess.

The economy of it appealed to you.

Yeah, and it teaches you really valuable lessons in one of the golden rules of writing: come in late and leave early.

So how old were you when you started writing these sketches?

Oh, I was writing them in my teens but no-one was ever seeing them. Then I wrote a sketch show when I was 18 for the charity week at school, and then went to drama school and was writing things like that there, and then left and started writing full-time as a sketch writer in London.

And what is the high point of your sketch writing career?

I probably can't say that, actually.

What does it involve?

Uhhh, I can't say that, actually.

Wow.

Some of the best stuff we wrote was for development and never got made but we sort of contributed to a few shows and things like that. And we just had a great, great time doing it because of course for every two lines that end up on the page, you've laughed pretty much for most of the day writing them with someone. Richard, the guy that I was writing with, is now in LA, but I know that we both have that memory of that time of just laughing all day every day.

Were there other feature scripts before Third Star?

Uh, yes. I wrote a film called Giltar Head, which I keep coming back to and thinking is there any life in that script, and before that was a script called Ding Dong Ray Ray Bell which has never seen the light of day, but I wrote it in LA for somebody. It was a coming of age story of a boy growing up in a mining town, which I liked a lot. Then Third Star came along.

Here's a question from Third Star's followers on Twitter: what was the genesis of the project? What was the first thing on your mind?

At the time I was being asked to develop TV series about guys in the army, and there were a lot of things happening in Afghanistan. There are great adventures to be written there, but they're also tricky because it's real people and it's based on a real situation that's still going on today. And the thing that struck me about the guys that are fighting now is they are just as brave as those who fought in the First and Second World Wars, but they are professional and did sign up to do it and that I wanted to write a story that felt like a Second World War movie about how normal guys could be asked by chance to do something incredibly brave. I wanted to come home to Wales to make a feature - I'd grown up in Pembrokeshire, and I'd had the idea based on a stag weekend that I'd had (where we didn't drown anyone) that it was a way to do this. That bringing in the element of somebody's right to die the way they want to could create that story of bravery for no other reason than friendship and camaraderie with ordinary boys.

So it was entirely on spec? No-one commissioned you?

No. I had been working in lots of other jobs in the industry and writing for other people and we decided that we wanted to go our own way and start a film company and I was the cheapest writer I could find.

That worked out well. So when you're starting a script, and when you started this script, do you outline everything or do you type Fade In and kind of work it out?

Well, I was working at that time with Adam Robertson, who plays Bill in the film. He's my best friend and he's also a producer as well. We had decided we were going to not make shorts, we were going to make a feature straight away. I sat in a cafe on the South Bank with him and said I've got this idea for a film: it's about four guys. The nature of Third Star is actually quite simple: it's a linear tale, it's a road movie, and so knowing what happens in the end and knowing who the four were in my head, it was actually quite simple to block out. It develops hugely over X million drafts but with that film it was quite easy to plot out. I don't think that's always possible, but I always try to. I think the more planning that goes into every single department, the better and scriptwriting is just one department of making a film.

Your four principals all have a shared history - are you the kind of writer that works out biographies for each one, or charts it out, because the script relies on those relationships and that history between them?

Yes, I do, but I really like to also get the actors involved in that. Having a theatre background myself, the rehearsal process there is so elongated and brilliant for that. The worst thing about filmmaking in many ways is that the actors are the last to come in at any stage of it, and we try to do that differently at Western Edge Pictures: to bring them in early. So as best as we could even though we had some movement in cast quite late in the day, we tried to involve them in that process. But I did definitely know sort of who the characters are, because we all end up doing jobs that we're sort of meant to do in some way or another, so it's written into the film what the boys have done. And I think the vaguest of those is James himself of course, because the illness has got the better of him at a key point in his life where he would have perhaps been making a career. So he hasn't gone into a career, but of course he wanted to be a writer and sees himself as some sort of literary god.

So you finish your first draft. Who's the first person who reads it that's not you?

Adam Robertson.

And how early did you let him in? Had you done several drafts?

Like most writers I promised it to him on a Friday to give myself a deadline, or on a Monday and I gave it to him on a Friday, late. We actually then read it together in the same cafe where I'd said I've got an idea, we should start a film company.

So you read it out loud together?

Yeah, we did. In an empty cafe. The two of us taking two parts each.

And being an actor, was he bookmarking his part?

Oh yeah, he knew he was going to be Bill, so he was obviously giving that some welly. And I was floundering with all the others.

As a trained actor yourself, were you ever thinking about performing in it?

No, really not. And they were so brilliant, those boys. I learned more from watching Tom Burke and Benedict in auditions, in three minutes, about the characters and about how the script should be, than I had in three months staring at the screen by myself.

D'you think the fact that you had been an actor affects how you write?

I hope so. I really really hope so. You know, Harrison Ford's classic line about the Star Wars script: you can write this shit, but you can't say it - I hope I have a better ear for dialogue than maybe some writers who haven't been an actor, because I know what it's like to go into an audition room and go, "Oh God, I don't know how to say this - this line's really awful". It may be the right meaning and in the right place and the right scene and everything, but just not a very good line. But there's more to it than that with those guys, in that they're so honed to deliver exactly the right performance of that character in that film of that story, that even though they may only be talking about their own part to start with, they know when something doesn't fit in the landscape - there's an anomaly - and they can make you see that. You're looking at the bigger picture and they'll go I've just fallen in a hole. It's here. And you go Oh yeah. God. So simple. I like actors to see the long version of the script because they know what I wanted to be going on in their heads, and then of course, comes the old theatre joke of I'll do it in a look, love. They really do convey so much in a look. And I think because I was an actor I feel really comfortable in giving them the power to do it in a look because it still feels like my script. I can just put a red line through that entire scene.

It's like them reading the original source-novel.

...Exactly.

It's been a while since shooting, but are there any anomalies or doing-it-in-a-look that you can remember?

The whole script is full of that. I mean really, I wouldn't even pick one out. It wasn't a very long script at the start - we added more action to it as we went on because we could, and lost big chunks of scenes that we just didn't need any more. Every single scene there was something that you'd find, even on the day, something didn't need to be said, because the look on Benedict's face, or Adam's face, or Tom's face, or JJ's face, was so good, you'd go, Ah, I don't want to hear them say any more - we know what's going on there; move on. And it was great. If only you could schedule that as a producer - if only I could schedule the looks, it would be cheaper.

So it eventually moves from being a script you're developing and reading with the actors and the cameras start rolling. But you're also the producer on the film, so how does that work? Do you completely take your writer hat off during production?

I did. Somebody else asked on Twitter: what was the best and worst, and it actually answers your question to answer that, in that I was completely Writer Hat Off. I mean, I was raising the finance, organising everything, putting out every fire every day all day. On the first day of the actual shoot we realised we weren't going to get the day and I was trying to work out how to fix it, knowing the sun was going down. The First [Assistant Director] on a set normally keeps time - most of the time for us, it was either the tide or the sun. The big First in the sky. I couldn't face that we weren't going to get the day the first time I was totally in charge on my own set. It was too much. And so I did a few producery tricks and did a bit of a Jedi Mind Trick on a few people, and we cut a few scenes, shot some scenes in a different location that didn't end up in the movie, and then put the boys in the back of my Land Rover. The scene that we were going to shoot next was like three pages long. I rewrote it as a half page scene and tossed the pages in the back as I drove through a field and immediately heard them saying, Oh yeah, no I can say that and you should say that and they sort of rewrote it again with what I'd done and we got out of the car and we shot it and we got that scene. It's not in the movie and I wish it was, but the sun was going down, and we'd got pretty much everything that was on the call sheet that day. Everyone was very happy and got in the trucks to go back to unit base in this beautiful location and as usual I sort of stayed behind to check that everything was clean and whatever, and the First came up to me and said, Oh well done, that was good, you got that, well done. And I thought Oh wow, we did - we got it and I had the incredible moment of feeling like a film producer - it was the best moment of my life. I'd fixed it and I'd been a writer and a producer that day, in that moment. And I also realised that it was a hair's breadth away from disaster. This was only the first day and I know how close we came to not doing that that day, and that's the worst knowledge to have - how close we came to disaster.

You want that to happen on like Day 54.

Exactly, exactly. So it was my worst moment as well. Because you're exhausted by the time you start, as the producer, you know, me and my co-producer Kelly Broad still had to bring it in. So one exact moment was best and worst, and then just so many after that. You're in your role and get used to it, but pretty much I was Producer Hat the whole way through filming. You mentioned going back to your beautiful location - this is not a random location for you. The film was not originally called Third Star.

No, it was called Barafundle Bay. And part of me still wishes it was. But it was a very strange thing that I may never have again where I not only thought we'll try and film it on the Pembrokeshire coast path somewhere, but I'll write that they'll sit on that step there, then he'll come down that path that's by it, because I can do it all from memory, and three and half years later, he's actually sitting on that step and walking down that path and it's exactly as I imagined it. So people would sort of come up to you, knowing the journey you've been on to get to the filming day: Aw, this must be really weird for you to be here, and it kind of wasn't in a way, because it was so totally what I imagined.

It's where I grew up, so I knew it all so well. There was a day where we were actually doing an interview like this at the top of the steps above Barafundle Bay, and a teacher of mine walked into shot and went Oh hi Vaughan and it really did bring it home to me. Every day, practically, somebody wandered across the coast path that I knew.

Was it something that you had in your head, as you were writing and producing: Oh, everyone I know will see this film?

No, I really didn't think about that. I had no idea and only very late in the producing process really, because you spend so long raising money, did I realise how much local support we would get. We had boats in frame that weren't there yesterday, kind of moored up in the night, and were able to phone the harbour master in Tenby and describe them: it's orange, and it's got a thing on a big aerial sticking out - Oh, that's Dave's, I'll call him now. And half an hour later the boat's gone. There were a million things, down to James' house being owned by friends of my father. Everything that I could have sort of milked from being local, being a local boy, we got. It was fantastic.

That's a pretty good way to make your first feature.

It really is. I recommend it to anyone. I mean, at times you also worry that you don't want anyone to be rude to anyone local, but they weren't.

You have to live with the consequences.

Exactly, I have to go back there. But no, as it was, we spent a lot of money locally, which I was glad about - local businesses did well out of us - and we got incredible support for it. And I think what's key about it is that things get filmed in Pembrokeshire an awful lot and have done over the years - Harry Potter had just been there, and Ridley Scott's Robin Hood had just been there, but they never shoot Pembrokeshire as Pembrokeshire, and of course Third Star is such a love letter to that bit of coast, which I think is the most beautiful place in the world. I'm very lucky to have been a lot of places in the world and I still think it's the most beautiful place in the world. So I was really pleased that we could do that.

It seems unfair that it never gets the credit. It stands in for beautiful things anywhere or in the fantasy world or something like that, but people should know ...

... it's Pembrokeshire. So that's my one regret, really, that it didn't get to be called Barafundle Bay, because it's why we went there.

Well, now people know. So obviously you survived the shoot - I'm sure you had more instances of rewrites and adjustments and things like that - does the film then change much in post-production, in the edit?

Oh yeah. Sometimes it feels like you don't start until you get in the edit, and things that everyone has fought hard to keep in the script just don't work. Either technical things went wrong or for some reason they don't work, and they're gone and suddenly what point they did tell in the story has to be replaced somewhere. So it changed - I say it changed a lot - it felt like it at times, but of course the magic of cinema is that you then watch it at the end and it's exactly the story you were going to tell. It's just a slightly different version. But we had

a disaster with some film stock being damaged in the lab, and so we had to do an insurance claim and a reshoot, and when we went down to do a reshoot just a few weeks later, the weather had changed completely: winter had set in. So we tried our best to shoot the stuff we needed to but we also just shot lots of atmospheric stuff of Benedict on his own on the shoreline with his hood up and the birds and the clouds, and a lot of that ended up in the edit going into James' darker nightmare of what was happening to him. It became a real key I think to the atmosphere of the film. So a mishap turned into a bonus.

There's a thread of being opportunistic ...

Exactly. There's not a film where that doesn't happen. And I love that.

That's that combination of writing and producing as well: oh we've got this guy for this day, so ...

Totally, yeah. And don't know what we'd have done really without that footage.

So the film is finished, it's released, it's screened in festivals worldwide. What are some of your favourite experiences or audiences to have watched it with?

Well, we're just about to release in Japan - Hi, Japan - and we're releasing in Germany at the moment. Somebody asked on Twitter when it's coming out there and will they be able to see it in the cinema? I hope so. We live in an age where you can contact your distributor and demand that you see it. I think there's every chance with this film that it will just roll on - I hope it does - so you will get the big screen thing, just to see Pembrokeshire looking so beautiful and the boys' big heads. In terms of my favourite things that happened, we actually closed The Edinburgh Film Festival, and Adam and I went up and had a very wild week in Edinburgh. We had the gala night, and the whole red carpet, and you know, that was pretty good. Adam and I had started the journey together with lots of beer and laughter and we ended it with a quite incredible amount of beer and laughter. And so there's that, but what I really loved in terms of release - these films are difficult to release and this one, thanks to the efforts of the team at Western Edge Pictures, has managed to get to an audience who've proved that there is a demand for it. They are really passionate, the fans, and they really love it in a way that has really touched us. It's just amazing.

They've produced some unexpected treasures for you as well.

The fan art has been incredible. And it's coming thick and fast. Yeah, we love it. We absolutely love it. So that's been really really touching. We've heard great stories of some really brave people who the film has touched. Other people of course just love Benedict because he's such a huge star. It's been a great journey. We went to some festivals, we had a great release, have done lots of nice interviews like this, but the ongoing support that it gets on Twitter and Facebook has been amazing, and it's the future of cinema, and that's why it's getting these re-releases and it's getting rolled out now and I'm sure that's why this book is going to be published - it's because of that love of the film that they've kept going, the fans have driven themselves.

How do you feel about the script being published now? How do you feel about the script itself, looking back on your work?

I'm really not precious about stuff, whether it's something I wrote yesterday that we're going to shoot tomorrow, or whether it's something I wrote back then that's survived. So I'm thrilled that Film Agency Wales, who've been the most incredible supporter throughout the whole process, are publishing it. I mean, when you said who read it first, after Adam, our exec producer Margaret Matheson read it second, and Film Agency Wales read it third and came straight in to support the film and me and have done so ever since. And they are absolutely the best regional film agency in the UK. They've got a great track record now and I hope it's the first of many scripts that they publish. So for me personally, would I write it again? No. Would I write it like that again? No, we all change, we all have different interests and get better I hope, but I'd be incredibly happy to think that some film student or English student will read it, to tear it apart and write essays about how wrong I got it. And they'd probably be right, but I think that's the value of this stuff, is to critique, and everyone gets better from it.

THIRD STAR

By

Vaughan Sivell

Western Edge Pictures Ltd

Supported by:

Film Agency For Wales
Asiantaeth Ffilm Cymru

FADE IN:

1 EXT. A CHURCH YARD 1

OPENING TITLE SEQUENCE

MUSIC

An extraordinarily green and lush rural graveyard.

CLOSE UP: Slow motion: The whirling head of a strimmer sweeps through the lush grass reaping it down to the roots. It moves over the contours of the old unkept graves sunken and rounded by time, knocking over small vases of flowers and keepsakes, some new some long-forgotten.

ANGLE ON:

MILES (29, handsome, possessing a natural confident charm; impeccably dressed in black) stares at a gravestone. He looks at the sky. Clear blue.

CUT TO:

2 EXT. OUTER-SPACE 2

Close in on James' face. (JAMES, 29, very thin.) He is very still. Behind him is a twinkling firmament in which he appears to be floating. He stares straight down the lens.

CUT TO:

3 INT. JAMES' HOUSE. PANTRY - DAY 3

DAVY (29, handsome, strong, earnest and trendy) stands holding an armful of jam jars, each filled with home made pickled produce. He is exasperated, but infinitely patient.

The alarm on Davy's watch goes off. He manages to turn it off and wonders how much longer this will take.

CUT TO:

4 EXT. JAMES' HOUSE - GARDEN 4

BILL (29, Scottish, an urban surf bum) emerges from the darkness of a barn. With what seems like Herculean strength he is carrying something above his head. We don't see all of it, just the general size of it and that it's some kind of mechanical contraption.

Bill is struggling to hold it aloft, with triumph, ceremony and excitement... Then sudden PANIC, as his arms judder.

CUT TO:

5 EXT. A CHURCH YARD 5

Miles, at the gravestone, lost in thought. Suddenly he starts getting hit by small flecks of greenery. In fact he's being splattered all over by them.

SMASH CUT:

A scruffy GROUNDSMAN, 55, wearing ear protectors and a face-shield, is strimming the grass of the churchyard with a petrol strimmer, edging backwards towards Miles. The strimmer is throwing up the mulched grass flecks.

Miles looks down at his smart clothes, now covered in grass as if this was somehow inevitable. The groundsman edges closer - still unaware of Miles. Miles pokes him lightly in the back. The groundsman turns round. Miles gestures with a slow sweep of his hand to show that he is covered in grass mulch.

The groundsman looks at the mess. He nods slowly with resignation. Using the same gesture he points out that his tattered old overalls are also covered.

Miles nods slowly. This is obviously going to be one of those days, weeks, months, years...

CUT TO:

6 EXT. OUTER-SPACE 6

Close in on James' face, floating in space.

He stares straight down the lens.

JAMES
James Kimberly Griffith.

He breaks into a laugh...

PULL OUT TO REVEAL:

James on his bed in front of a huge poster of the firmament, holding a small camera in front of himself.

Davy enters carrying James' shoes. James shows him the images on the camera.

DAVY
Your mum just made me do CPR on one of Chloe's old dolls.

JAMES
At least one of us is getting
some.

Davy nods. Resigned.

JAMES (CONT'D)
Do you know CPR?

James looks at the shoes. With one hand in each, he 'tap dances' them on the tray table beside him.

DAVY
No. But that doll did give me a
semi.

JAMES
If I didn't know better, Sherpa
Davy, I'd say you've cleaned
these shoes.

Davy smiles and shrugs as he starts sorting out his medication almost like a croupier with chips and cards. Swift and professional.

James puts on one shoe himself. But he is struggling with the other. Davy sees and comes over to help.

CUT TO:

7 INT. JAMES' HOUSE BATHROOM. 7

CHLOE (30, James' sister, naturally beautiful) leans against the wall, crying. She looks in the mirror. She tries to take a deep breath. She can't. At the sink she splashes her face and leaves the bathroom...

8 JAMES' HOUSE. HALL (CONTINUED) 8

Chloe checks her watch. Her little girl(5) runs to her. She scoops her up, hugs her too hard. Mrs Griffith marches past.

MRS GRIFFITH
Lord knows where the drinks table-

Seeing Chloe's face she does a double-take.

MRS GRIFFITH (CONT'D)
Have you looked in a mirror?

CHLOE
Yes. I -

MRS GRIFFITH
Oh. Well.

Then she walks on. Chloe is a bit smacked in the face for a moment, then takes a breath.

CHLOE
Let's help Granny with the party.

CUT TO:

9 EXT. JAMES' HOUSE. GARDEN. 9

Still seeing only part of the contraption, including one of its shiny wheels and a tyre, Bill and MR GRIFFITH (James' father, 65, vague engineering genius) stare at it.

BILL
You've done it, Mr. Griff... now ANYTHING is possible.

Long pause. Mr Griffith seems to seriously consider this and conclude that the statement can't be accurate.

MR GRIFFITH
Well...

They stare at the cart. Mr Griffith kicks a tyre gently.

CUT TO:

10 EXT. JAMES' GARDEN 10

James sits on a garden chair and looks back at the house where a lunch party is in full swing. Family and friends fill the house. James' mother and Chloe pass around food at his family and friends. Bill tucks into mountains of food as he talks to Chloe's husband MIKE (He is 40, gentle, square). He looks bored.

Chloe's children examine Mr Griffith's face scientifically as he explains wrinkles.

Mrs Griffith and Davy check the taste of a salad dressing. Davy suggesting a little more balsamic.

Chloe and Mrs Griffiths put food out, side by side. Chloe adjusts the plate layout and immediately Mrs Griffith swaps it back round and walks out. James chuckles and looks at the sky...

CUT TO:

11 EXT. JAMES' HOUSE. DRIVEWAY. 11

Miles gets out of his Jaguar. He seems a little uncomfortable about the number of other cars.

He walks to the house trying to brush from his clothes the remaining grass mulch.

CUT TO:

12 EXT. JAMES' GARDEN - DAY 12

Miles comes to the conservatory unaware that James has seen him. Davy and Bill go to greet him with cheers.

Chloe's two little girls rush to him. He picks them up and showers them with unashamed affection. He puts them down and hugs Chloe and shakes her husband's hand.

Miles has a charming word for everyone. He's greeted with love and laughter by all, but then he sees James...

Miles' face betrays a moment of shock at James' appearance. He approaches and sits in a chair opposite.

They look at each other in silence with malevolent enigmatic power barely contained (before engaging in their normal meaningless banter...)

JAMES
Miles.

MILES
You look like shit. I thought they'd stuck you out here 'cos you'd snuffed it.

JAMES
Having a pretty good day rhabdomyosarcoma-wise -

MILES
You, You, You. Jesus...

James laughs.

JAMES
How are you? You look amazing.

MILES
Thank you, James. I think you're right.

They look at each other...

JAMES
Wish me Happy Birthday.

MILES
Shit. Is it your birthday?

James smiles. Davy and Bill approach. Bill has his stills camera.

BILL
(To Miles)
You wearing that blouse on the expedition?

MILES
Don't even start. (To James) And why are you dressed as the bass player in an 80's pop group?

Chloe appears with drinks...

BILL
Chloe, perfect creature!... Take a photo of us... Together again.

Chloe puts down the drinks. Takes the camera from Bill. They pose for the shot.

BILL (CONT'D)
(Taking camera and a drink)
Thanks, beautiful. Come on Miles let's get wankered and embarrass ourselves.

CHLOE
You look well, Miles! What's the secret?

MILES
None of your business, cock breath! Pour me a drink.

BILL
Nobody move!

As Bill runs off to the barn...

CHLOE
Now, be nice you three, he's really excited about this!

Chloe puts her arm round James.

JAMES
After Auntie Jane's leg warmers I'd be excited if Bill gave me a yeast infection - (Seeing Bill's gift) Oh Christ.

Bill returns carrying a tree sapling with its roots wrapped in hessian. It's about eight feet tall.

BILL
This is a tree.

Silence.

BILL (CONT'D)
I grew this tree - FROM SEED!

JAMES
(Realising Bill awaits reaction)
Oh! Holy shit!

Davy and Miles snort their drinks in unexpected laughter.

BILL
WE are taking this tree to Barafundle Bay.

Davy raises his eyebrows.

JAMES
A larch?

BILL
GOOD! I'm going to make sure it grows there forever.

JAMES
Bill... I love it. Thank you.

They admire the tree in silence for a while.

MILES
PLEASE say it, Davy.

DAVY
How are we going to carry it? (Trying not to upset him) It is a brilliant, brilliant idea.

MILES
Brilliant.

DAVY
Brilliant. Lovely. But I think we are going to struggle with all the other stuff anyway.

MILES
Lovely idea.

Chloe cuffs him.

BILL
I can carry it. Or it can go on the cart. It'll be easy.

CHLOE
I think you underestimate the difficulties of this adventure -

BILL
We're taking you to your favourite place on earth! You're going to see it going into the ground... and nothing and no one is going to stop me.

BEAT. Miles raises his eyebrows - not sure what else to do. Davy takes a small present from his pocket.

DAVY
OK... well at least mine is small.

MILES
I heard some girls like that. I've never met one but -

Laughter. James unwraps it and sees a battered penknife.

JAMES
I can't take this, Davy... I gave him this when we were -

DAVY
Ten.

Chloe is moved and looks away. Miles looks at her.

BILL
Miles? (To James) I hope you like sports cars, you lucky wee bastard.

Miles scoffs at this. He hands an envelope to James...

MILES
Go mad.

JAMES
A year's subscription to Playboy... and a cheque for ten million pounds - posted dated to 2012.

They laugh.

MILES
It's the least I could do.

DAVY
It is.

They laugh but Miles and Davy dart a look to each other noting the sting... Mr Griffith joins them.

MR GRIFFITH
Miles! So tell me about her?

Miles looks bewildered.

MR GRIFFITH (CONT'D)
The new one?

MILES
I'm single.

Chloe exits, to see her girls playing.

MR GRIFFITH
What? (There is a moment of confusion) No! The new Jag!

MILES
Oh - yeah. You should take it for a spin while we're gone.

MR GRIFFITH
I will! No. I won't. Mrs. G's gone green... Objects to the lawn mower!

BILL
You should eco-equate like me.

MILES
Half man - half compost heap?

BILL
HEY! Come and look at the go-cart!

Miles' mobile rings. He looks at the display.

MILES
Sorry better take this.

He walks away from them towards his car.

MR GRIFFITH
(mumbly, non-communicative)
Just got to fit the brakes... couldn't get the bonding to... And ... I'm still not sure it's wise...

Davy helps James to his feet. As Miles walks away he sees this and looks away. Bill goes towards the barn and they follow.

CUT TO:

13 EXT. JAMES' HOUSE. DRIVEWAY. MILES' CAR. 13

Miles walks to his car. He looks stressed as he listens. He opens the boot while he's talking...

MILES
Mac. What's the story?... Except the money isn't there. So, we can't just tell the board....

He takes his overnight bag. When he shuts the boot he sees Chloe, with her husband, Mike, and their young girls blowing bubbles. The sun is shining through Chloe's summer skirt. She looks at Miles and smiles.

MILES (CONT'D)
(Still on the phone)
What will we have by Tuesday?!... It was mine to lose, Mac. We did everything right... We'll see. Bye.

Miles ends the call and shakes his head. He looks at the view. He struggles to take a deep breath. He is obviously not coping too well behind his smile. He takes out his mobile. He types out a text... "I LOVE YOU." Then he deletes it without sending it. He shakes his head. He tries to breathe deeply again but it seems he can't fill his lungs.

CUT TO:

14 INT. JAMES' HOUSE. THE BARN - DAY 14

James is sitting on the cart. Mr Griffith, Bill and Davy are admiring what we now see is a go-kart, that Bill was carrying earlier. It is built from what is obviously an old go-kart, but with new shining wheels and handles attached to push it from behind. It has "APOLLO 18" painted on it. The boys examine it with quiet wonder. Miles comes in as the others try out the pushing handles.

BILL
This is going to be an amazing trip.

DAVY
(To Miles)
Well, Jim's been really strong for the last few weeks, even eating.

BILL
(To Miles)
Have you ever seen anything so awesome in your life?

Davy's watch alarm beeps.

DAVY
Meds Jim.

They head toward the house. James stops for a second.

JAMES
(To Miles)
Thanks for coming.

MILES
Twat.

James walks on smiling.

CUT TO:

15 INT. JAMES' LIVING ROOM - DAY 15

MUSIC. The party. The lights dim. Mrs Griffith enters with the cake. They sing Happy Birthday, but we don't hear it. Chloe is beside her husband.

James eyes the candles. He wafts his hand through the orange flames. He bends down towards the flames, takes a huge breath and...

CUT TO:

16 EXT. VIEW FROM THE GARDEN. 16

A fiery sunset. Orange sky. Wales is green and pleasant.

In the garden is one of his father's beautiful wind powered sculptures, in the shape of a ship and fish, shimmering, tinkling as it slowly spins.

A deflated birthday balloon is caught in a tree where it bobs in the wind.

CUT TO:

17 INT. JAMES' BEDROOM -EVENING 17

James is in bed. His father sticks his head round the door.

MR GRIFFITH
Night, Jim.

JAMES
Dad?

He enters and comes to James' bed.

JAMES (CONT'D)
My sixth birthday, I'm sorry I used the lining of your suit to make my Action Man's parachute.

Mr Griffith looks confused then remembers and nods.

JAMES (CONT'D)
Mum went mad. You didn't.

MR. GRIFFITH
I was *livid.* I want to hit you *now.*

James laughs, but he's tired. Mr Griffith looks at the floor. But he puts his hand on James' face and holds it there for a moment. He just can't speak... He goes to leave.

Then Mr Griffith stops and turns around.

MR GRIFFITH
When we nearly lost you, even as I dived into the sea, my mind was racing ahead. Even in the panic, my mind was playing out how I'd try to live without you... and I couldn't. And the water was like treacle. And then you weren't moving and I passed you up to the people in the boat, and I didn't watch...

JAMES
It's funny. I think I remember. It was peaceful.

MR GRIFFITH
I doubt it. You were three.... If you hadn't spluttered your way back I don't think I'd have come back from the water either... I mean, I would have... I would have been walking, breathing... but drowned, for the rest of my life... Then you were OK. Crying.
(MORE)

MR GRIFFITH (CONT'D)
Shocked. And OK. And...I thought -
I thought we'd taken your
gamble... and we'd won.

James nods.

MR GRIFFITH (CONT'D)
We don't like morbidity in this
house.

Mrs Griffith comes in and sets about the night-time routine with her military style.

MR GRIFFITH (CONT'D)
Good night.
(All totally straight
faced)
Yes. I just... Well, OK. The chap
next door is putting a green
house in the sight line of my
workshop. I'm going to surf the
net to find a hitman. Have him
killed. Butchered.

JAMES
OK.

He exits.

MRS GRIFFITH
Right. Well, kitchen is closed.
So let's get you sorted.

She plumps his pillows too vigorously. He lies back already drowsy.

JAMES
Thank you.

On the wall beside his head is a map of a coast line and some pictures of cliff tops.

JAMES (CONT'D)
I can't wait to get out of here.

MRS GRIFFITH
You know what I think of this
trip... I'm going to unpack some
of your boxes while you're away.
Get this room sorted.

JAMES
Oh, don't touch my things!

MRS. GRIFFITH
Fine! You do it.

JAMES
You can unpack that box. It's all pornography.

She just gets on with sorting out his meds, muttering to herself. She picks up a bookmarked copy of James And The Giant Peach as she tidies.

MRS. GRIFFITH
I won't read tonight....

He closes his eyes.

MRS. GRIFFITH (CONT'D)
Night, angel boy.

She goes to the door. Only now does her sadness show, she exits leaving James in the gloom of his room.

CUT TO:

18 EXT. UNDER THE OCEAN 18

The gloom of the water with sun streaming through from above... Suddenly the surface breaks... amidst the bubbling turmoil a three year-old-boy, in shorts and T-shirt, sinks under the water, kicking and reaching, through the bubbles.

19 EXT. JAMES' HOUSE - JUST AFTER DAWN 19

A bottle of champagne is sprayed over the go-kart to a cheer from the boys.

The go-kart is strapped to the roof of Bill's Land Rover. There is exuberant chaos as Davy, Miles and Bill bicker with each other and with Chloe and Mrs Griffith about where to pack things! Mrs Griffith tries to organise the food she has prepared, which is packed in a miraculous amount of Tupperware.

MRS GRIFFITH
The lettuce for today's sandwiches is loose in this bag. Are you listening?

ANGLE ON: Miles, really angry, pointing at something else.

MILES
NO! NO WAY! I only agreed to the whole trip on this ONE condition!

JAMES
(Laughing)
Miles -

MILES
NO! Bill is not taking that!

Only now do we see Bill is holding his guitar.

DAVY
(Laughing too)
Bill, we did promise him and I -
just don't think I can stomach it
either.

Bill relents, much to the stifled amusement of James'
parents and Chloe, and takes it to the house sourly.

BILL
(Under his breath)
Can't kill the music inside me.

DAVY
He's repellent isn't he?

James' mother gives them a large polka dot, deflated lilo.
Miles is shadow boxing her annoyingly. Davy tries to
wrestle the tree up through the sunroof as Bill comes out
and shouts at him to treat it gently. James surveys the
chaos with ultimate pleasure.

Finally they are ready. James shakes his brother-in-law's
hand warmly. Then hugs Chloe.

CHLOE
Have fun.

Mike puts a hand on her shoulder.

James looks at his father. His father opens his mouth as if
to speak, but changes his mind.

JAMES
(Looking at him
curiously)
You have never bored me.

Mr Griffith's face is transformed by the most charming
smile.

MR GRIFFITH
I never meant to.

They laugh and James hugs him.

NEAR BY

Bill is on his phone having a strained argument.

BILL
Abbie... Abbie! I did say I'd be away three or four days... OR FOUR! Darling-

Davy rolls his eyes at Miles as they pack.

NEAR BY

James turns to his mother.

MRS GRIFFITH
(Loudly)
Don't be mouthy to people just because Miles is there.

JAMES
You know I could never keep still? I have to feel like I'm on my way somewhere...

MRS GRIFFITH
Ha! Don't I?!

JAMES
Do you?

Mrs Griffith looks confused, starts to well up, but fights the urge fiercely.

MRS. GRIFFITH
I'm glad you explored.
(Whispering)
I love you.

JAMES
Christ, you annoy me.

She laughs. They look at each other warmly. He lightly kisses her.

He is about to get in the car when he looks to Chloe again. She is just keeping it together. He darts back towards her. She rushes at him and they hug... Then he gets into the car.

MRS GRIFFITH
(to Bill and Davy)
Bill, Davy, take the utmost care!

MILES
What about me?!

Mrs Griffith gives Miles a weary look.

JAMES
Westward Ho, boys bach!

MILES
Your mum's the only ho'...

The boys laugh raucously. The car speeds away with her calling after.

MRS GRIFFITH
No risks! Not the slightest! Be-

She stops. They are out of earshot. Mr Griffith puts an arm round her.

CUT TO:

20 EXT. MAIN ROAD - DAY 20

The car heads west, music playing.

CUT TO:

21 EXT. PEMBROKESHIRE COUNTRYSIDE, NARROW LANES - DAY 21

They drive along chatting and laughing, music playing.

The window is open and James shuts his eyes and lets the wind and the sunlight play on his face.

CUT TO:

22 EXT/INT. THE CAR IN THE COUNTRYSIDE - DAY 22

James looks at the boys in the car. Bill grooves to some music, Davy reading the map. Miles sleeps.

As James watches Miles, Miles' eyes slowly open. He looks straight at James for a moment, then lets his eyes close.

CUT TO:

23 EXT/INT. PEMBROKESHIRE COUNTRYSIDE. BILL'S CAR - DAY 23

NEAR THE COAST. Davy drives. They see the sparkling sea. James stares at it.

CUT TO:

24 EXT. NATIONAL PARK'S CAR PARK - DAY 24

The boys have unloaded. Nearby a fat family are sunbathing and having a picnic beside their car (string vests, and scotch eggs). They watch the boys with suspicion.

James sits on the grass as Bill tries to rig up the tree on the cart, while Davy weighs up each back pack. They have way too much stuff.

BILL
Put it over the back wheels!

DAVY
But we need more weight at the front!

Miles watches James test his bad leg. But Davy pushes the go-kart towards James.

DAVY (CONT'D)
I can get that other cushion-

JAMES
Not yet. I want to start under my own steam!

James sets off. The others look at one another and follow.

BILL
How bloody beautiful is this?!

MILES
Do we have to get to a certain point tonight?

Bill shakes his head.

BILL
We'll cross to the island, walk until... well until James-

Miles stops. He watches for a moment. He looks down the path behind them and then out at the sea. He tries to take a deep breath but his chest is tight.

DAVY
I don't want to be knackered and hungry before we put up the tents.

BILL
Don't stress! Look at the sky, the hedgerow...

DAVY
While you're examining the hedgerow I have to think about how James... (He and James exchange a glance) is actually going to get sorted out each night.

Miles looks ahead at the three and the cart, he is uneasy, but he follows.

CUT TO:

25 EXT. CLIF TOP - PATHS. MORNING. 25

In the background James sits on the grass watching something off screen and he claps rhythmically.

In the foreground Miles and Davy lie inexplicably close together on their backs in silence, beside the base of a bush.

Suddenly Bill flies through the air above them brushing the top of the bush. He grunts with pain as he lands and rolls.

James cheers and laughs hysterically.

Miles rummages in his pocket, takes out a ten pound note and gives it to Davy. They get up.

In the background Bill gets to his feet in pain but triumphant.

BILL
YEAH!!! I'm super-fucking-human!

Davy and Miles laughing, join James.

JAMES
It won't get better than this!

Davy looks at him. James' face betrays a double meaning.

Davy's smiles fades and he looks at the ground. Bill and Miles' smiles fade too and they look at James and Davy...

JAMES (CONT'D)
We may as well confront it. I know all know...

He looks at Miles. Miles looks out at the sea.

JAMES (CONT'D)
Six months.

BILL
My brother's mate's mum had six months and she's doing fine and that was five years ago! You have to stay positive. Yes? Yes!

James smiles at him.

JAMES
I'm OK. I'm really, really, OK.

Silence. James looks at Miles again. So does Davy - willing him to say something... He doesn't.

JAMES (CONT'D)
We'd better keep moving, eh?

Bill springs up.

BILL
Yes!

James, turns on the small radio on the cart. He takes a deep breath and sets off as fast as he can. Quietly the boys follow....

CUT TO:

26 EXT. CLIFF TOP PATHS - DAY 26

From a distance we see the boys coming over a hill. The wide countryside on one side, the endless sea on the other.

The cliff top is relatively flat and grassy. Bill eats a sandwich.

JAMES
...I mean breast cancer isn't funny but mammogram is one of the funniest words ever!

They laugh.

DAVY
(to Miles)
Do you ever see Laura?

Miles looks sharply at him, and laughs shallowly.

James listens with acute interest, observing Miles.

MILES
She's all clear apparently.

BILL
She would've been down the aisle with you -

MILES
She's with a banker of some kind. Probably choosing dinner plates already.

DAVY
She was amazing... Good luck to her. Probably best...

Miles' throat tightens and Davy sees it. So does James.

MILES
I don't know anything about
anything.

DAVY
Aaah! The disarming self-
deprecation! Good spin.

MILES
Advertising in the blood. Guilty.

BILL
(Loving his sandwich)
Anyone who doesn't love beetroot
is -

JAMES
-a deviant. (In pain but lying)
May as well try this out.

James climbs into the go-kart. Miles doesn't help him. Davy rushes forward. Davy and the others exchange a look of concern about James' strength.

JAMES (CONT'D)
Excellent! This will be just
fine!

The boys look at him. He looks ridiculous. Miles and Davy take the handles at the back and they move off.

BILL
Loving this! LOVING THIS!

Bill, totally over excited, tears his shirt off and starts skipping along ahead of them, at one with nature.

CUT TO:

27 EXT. CLIFF TOP PATHS - DAY 27

An elderly couple are having a picnic looking at the sea. The boys come over the brow of a hill. Bill naked and leading. Davy and Miles push James in the cart. The old couple stare in amazement.

BILL
Hello. Beautiful isn't it?

JAMES
(Smiling radiantly)
Hello!

DAVY
Hello.

MILES
Hello.

They walk on out of sight.

CUT TO:

28 EXT. PATHWAY THROUGH WOODLAND 28

James leans on Davy for support while James tries to urinate in the hedge.

JAMES
Did Miles already know how long?

DAVY
No. I don't think so.

James nods thinking about this.

DAVY (CONT'D)
Taking you to piss always makes me want to piss, and you piss far more than I used to, so where's all my new piss coming from? I'm not drinking more-

JAMES
Will you shut the fuck up!

BEAT. Davy and James stare into space.

At last James urinates.

Nearby... Bill and Miles have some tea, brewed on Bill's camp stove, and biscuits. They look over to James then to each other and say nothing. Bill tops up his tea with hot water. It's not as good now, so he dunks his biscuit.

BILL
Biscuits - they're great on their own... but once they get dipped in tea they become a whole different journey.

Miles laughs.

BILL (CONT'D)
A make-up girl at work was reading one of your dad's books. The Lebanon Tree.

Miles nods.

BILL (CONT'D)
How's your book coming?

Miles is uncomfortable.

MILES
Gave up on it. Couldn't be arsed.

BILL
You should just write a diary
about banging Chelsea-chicks.

MILES
Finally bored of meaningless sex.

BILL
Bollocks. Later. I want to be
lying back with a beer. Then I
want a tale of orifice that would
make most people go blind.

MILES
I'll scan the memory banks.

BILL
This cart is the business. I want
one! I could fit a sail to it. I
want to go to try land yachting
in Baja, Mexico. Saw it on TV.
Looks amazing. Man! I know she's
not pretty, but she'll go all the
way, I know it.

MILES
Speaking of which, how's Abbie?
Why wasn't she at the party?

BILL
Well, she had a thing for work
that... she had to... uh... do.
It was tricky.

MILES
(Not convinced)
Right.

BILL
(With some hesitance)
No, it's all good. It's all good.
It's all good.

MILES
Good. Now - again with feeling.

On Davy and James.

DAVY
I may as well piss now too.

He turns to urinate still holding James steady. James glances down at Davy's urine as he starts to urinate. He looks alarmed and back at Davy.

DAVY (CONT'D)
Probably the beetroot....
(reassuring himself) ....Yeah.

CUT TO:

29 EXT. THE LILY POND BRIDGE 29

Davy and Bill carry the cart over the narrow footbridge bridge as James and Miles walk slowly along behind.

DAVY
Every so often I check the credits and wait for the camera man...

BILL
It's not Shakespeare, but it pays the mortgage.

DAVY
Mate, Grand Designs has a big audience!

BEAT. Bill grins and nods.

BILL
I work on DIY SOS.

DAVY
Oh sorry.... (confused) Are you sure? Well, that's better... isn't it?

CUT TO:

30 EXT. WOODLAND PATH NEAR GROTTO 30

Suddenly the cart lurches and the boys stop.

BILL
Woah! Shit!

JAMES
Cart malfunction everyone!

Bill and Davy examine the damaged axle.

DAVY
I knew it! It's the weight I'm telling you!

MILES
Is it fucked?

BILL
Not on my shift.

Bill starts unloading the kit...

CUT TO:

31 EXT. WOODLAND PATH/OR GROTTO 31

Davy is tightening the wheels on the cart.

Bill is stowing some stuff in an undercover grotto nearby. He looks back at the boys and then goes into the backpacks and starts hurriedly, secretly, taking out all the spare clothes.

BILL
(To himself)
They won't let me have my guitar? They can't have their fashion show. Essentials only...

Nearby, as Davy starts reloading, Miles sits with James looking at the view.

MILES
You've honestly, honestly, never watched that Green Peace footage of baby seals getting clubbed and thought... yeah. Cruel. Ban it - but just after I've had a go.

James roars with laughter... Bill rejoins Davy.

DAVY
I decide, in the confusion of whether he's joking or not, that he probably is.

BILL
Mate! HE doesn't even know if he's joking.

Back to Miles and James...

JAMES
How's work actually going?

Miles looks at him with suspicion.

MILES
You hate what I do.

JAMES
Only because you do. Are you
writing?

As we listen to them we see Bill in the background finish with the cart and struggle loading the tree.

MILES
I'm so bored of the Laura and 'my
book' questions. I'm not a
writer, Jim. I'm an ad' man. I'm
good at it. Let's just talk about
nice stuff.

DAVY
(To James)
Don't get angry, but I promised
I'd phone your mum in a while.

JAMES
Jesus! We only just left!

DAVY
I know. I promised.

JAMES
Tell her we have hope in our
hearts and wings on our heels!
And after that - no more calling!
(To Miles) And if you've got your
mobile on you I'll bloody find
it.

MILES
I haven't!

JAMES
Bill. We could just plant that -

BILL
No!

CUT TO:

32 EXT. NEAR THE WHITE BULL - DAY 32

The boys descend over the hill and see The White Bull. A fisherman's tavern on a small quayside nestled in a tiny cove. There's a celebration in progress, a small colourful, pagan festival. A pig is roasting on an open spit. The locals stand around near the quay in front of the pub.

BILL
Perfect!

JAMES
Push me on Davy! Push me on Miles!

Davy and Miles smile at each other and do as they're told.

DAVY
My 'Spidey Senses' are tingling.

JAMES
Herpes, Davy. You've been Boybanding some Pill-ripened, teen mum-to-be again, haven't you?

DAVY
When do I have time to do that?

JAMES
Admit it! You whoremaker!

CUT TO:

33 EXT. THE WHITE BULL - DAY 33

The boys get some funny looks as they move through the mini-festival. The locals are letting their hair down. A band (young and very good) are playing on the back of a trailer. Bill loves it. Davy is worried that people will bump James, and acts as a human shield. James and Miles look around bemused.

A flat bed lorry is decorated with hay bales and streamers. A large throne is empty in the middle and a crown lies abandoned on the seat. Amongst the locals are some costumed characters (a GOAT, a BEAR, a strange HUMAN TREE carrying a horn that he blows drunkenly from time to time, and a small boy dressed as an ANGEL).

The boys find a few bales to sit on near the edge of it all and bask in the atmosphere. Davy takes the silver meds kit out. James shakes his head. Davy doesn't like it but puts the meds away.

BILL
Fuck, it's good to be back here! I'll get the beers in.

Bill bounds off towards the bar.

JAMES
I'll have a Guinness!

Bill hesitates for a second then nods. James looks at Davy for a moment who stops himself from objecting.

JAMES (CONT'D)
I hope something really... WILD happens.

DAVY
How wild?

JAMES
Dangerously wild.

DAVY
Eat some under-cooked pig?... (Looking at the crowd) This is pretty wild.

JAMES
I know, but we're just watching. I want to do something extreme!

As Miles heads towards the pub...

MILES
You want to get laid?

JAMES
No. I just - let's not rule that out - but I want a thrill, a MAN-THRILL, I want trouble...

DAVY
We could steal a boat.

JAMES
Now we're talking!

DAVY
No.

James smiles reluctantly but he looks around at the young couples chatting each other up, at the families laughing and drinking, and eating...

CUT TO:

34 INT. THE WHITE BULL. TOILET - DAY 34

Miles stares in the mirror. He takes off his Rolex. He puts it down by the sink. He washes his face and hands. He's struggling again. He takes a deep breath but he can't seem to fill his lungs. He exits, but leaves his Rolex watch by the sink.

As he exits, the Angel-boy pushes past him into the toilets.

The door closes behind Miles.

He walks on and goes to look at his watch... He rushes back in to the toilet.

He goes to the sink. The watch is gone. He kicks open the cubicle doors, but the cubicles are empty. As the last of the doors flies open a white feather wafts into the air. Miles looks at it then exits in a hurry.

CUT TO:

35 EXT. THE WHITE BULL 35

James see Miles emerge, searching for the Angel-Boy, frantically weaving through the crowd.

Bill dances with some locals.

Miles catches a glimpse of the Angel-Boy, but can't catch up.

James looks at him and sees a white feather drifting in the wind. It wafts down towards him... as he reaches out for it a hand grabs it. It's Miles. He looks at the feather, then both he and James see a glimpse of the white wings heading towards the quayside. Miles follows.

36 EXT. WHITE BULL QUAYSIDE 36

Eventually Miles follows him to the edge of the quayside but the boy has vanished. It doesn't seem possible. Miles turns through 360 degrees. Then he see the tops of the wings emerging over the quayside as the boy climbs up a mooring ladder, holding a basket with a bottle in it. He looks at Miles and then sits down nonchalantly on a hay bale and takes a swig of his sea chilled cider. On the boy's wrist is a gleaming Rolex.

BOY
What are you looking at?

MILES
Where'd you get that watch?

BOY
My father. Birthday present. It's a Rolex Oyster, Professional Sea-Dweller 4000.

MILES
Your dad's a liar. It's a fake.

BOY
Fuck you.

MILES
Nice. Give it to me.

BOY
I'm going to tell him you asked to see my cock.

MILES
Go on then.

BOY
(wicked grin)
Do you like my wings?

MILES
Give me that watch or I'll rip them off and use the blood on their stumps to write-

BOY
(Enthralled)
Write what?

MILES
Thief.

BOY
I don't want this watch anymore... I don't like fakes.

MILES
Me neither.

The boy throws the watch in the water.

BOY
Then we're both better off.

Miles registers this with contained exasperation. Miles turns to leave.

BOY (CONT'D)
What's up with your bumchum in the cart?

MILES
Sick.

BOY
Is he your best mate?

MILES
Yes.

The boy swigs some cider.

MILES (CONT'D)
How old are you?

BOY
Nearly eleven.

The boy seems bored of him all of a sudden.

MILES
You may be tough, but being a
'grown up' is shit -

BOY
Piss off! If I wanted chick-flick
advice from some paedo - I'd go
to church.

MILES
You'll be dead before you're
thirty.

Miles walks away.

BOY
Hey, poofter!

Miles turns.

BOY (CONT'D)
What time is it?

Miles instinctively looks at his watch. It's not there...
The boy chuckles devilishly. Miles is beaten. He smiles.

CUT TO:

37 EXT. BACK NEAR THE FESTIVAL - DAY 37

Bill is dancing enthusiastically. Miles returns and offers
the feather to James.

JAMES
You keep it.

Miles looks at it and tucks in his pocket. He takes a beer
from a tray.

Suddenly near to Bill, two young lads start fighting. A
girl screams and Bill decides to step in.

BILL
Brothers! This is not the way!

Bill tries to wrench one lad clear, but in doing so he
accidentally elbows a fat girl in the face. She screams and
falls. He looks at her in confusion. Another guy leaps at
Bill and punches him. Bill barely flinches (gentle Bill is
extremely hard). The boys know this. They've seen this
happen before.

DAVY
He's like an Alsatian pup. He's one of those guys that EVERYONE just seems to love.

While protesting his innocence Bill floors his assailant. He is surrounded. Punches and furniture are flying from all around. Bill wrestles under a pile of angry locals.

MILES
Nuts?

He offers the nuts. The boys watch a while longer, then Miles sighs. He downs most of his pint and calmly walks toward the fight and wades in, elbowing punching, and trying to pull people off Bill.

Davy tuts and shakes his head.

DAVY
Back in a minute.

JAMES
Davy, I'm going in!

DAVY
Are you drunk?

JAMES
A little. This is IT!

DAVY
You should probably sit this out.

JAMES
NO! Bollocks![Desperate. He realises he can't move. He looks back at Davy) Davy, ramming speed!

Davy knows this is a bad idea.

JAMES (CONT'D)
Please. We can do this. We can BLOODY DO THIS!

BEAT.

Davy rolls his eyes. This is a bad idea but he goes behind the go-kart and starts pushing James towards the fight as fast as he can. As they hurtle into the fray James grabs a stool and brandishes it in front of him. He roars as he ploughs into a group of men trying to get at Bill.

Miles and Bill are doing OK, until Miles accidentally punches an old woman in the face.

ANGRY LOCAL BRAWLER
What's wrong with you bastards?
Stop hittin' the women!

Miles is hit on the nose. He's blinded and flailing around badly. Davy fights beside James trying to protect himself and James. James, still in the cart, swings the stool, trying to hurt people in any way he can, but he's soon exhausted. Someone punches him. Davy is livid.

DAVY
Hey! Not him! He's got cancer!
I'm not shitting with you! You
don't hit people with cancer!

A few people stop and stare. Miles takes the chance to hit someone, but Davy grabs the cart and pulls James away. Bill grabs Miles and pulls him away and they join Davy and push the cart as fast they can away from the crowd who are still fighting each other.

The boys grab their packs and the tree as they run.

DAVY (CONT'D)
Leave it Bill, for God's-

BILL
NO!

A couple of drunken locals and the one dressed as the Bear stagger after them, but soon give up, hurling abuse instead.

The boys make it to the lane and away over the hill, still running.

DISSOLVE TO:

38 EXT. A STREAM - DAY 38

They stop to wash their faces. Davy has a bloody nose and lip. Miles tenderly nurse his jaw. Bill whips off his shirt and splashes cool water over himself. Gradually the other two strip off too. Davy gets some pills out of the silver Meds kit for James.

BILL
Aaaah! That's good...

DAVY
My teeth are actually fizzing.
One of my ears is ringing.

Davy, Miles and Bill examine their scrapes and scratches, and apply antiseptic ointment to each other.

BILL
Crystal water, man-flesh and antiseptic. Every Welshman's dream.

DAVY
This is the gayest thing we've ever done.

MILES
I feel so free -

DAVY
I have an insight into what it's like to be one of your wank-puppets.

MILES
Pretty great - I imagine.

Davy and Miles nurse themselves further.

James winces with silent pain and takes a huge swig of morphine syrup secretly.

Bill gets out his video camera. James takes the camera and starts fooling around with it filming himself...

MILES (CONT'D)
How's the new camera!

BILL
No... I didn't get - We had a new bathroom instead.

Miles and Davy exchange glances at this.

James stares down the lens, then turns the camera on the boys and the view around them.

JAMES
"It seems to me my lord that the present life of men here on earth is as though a sparrow in the winter time should come to a house and very swiftly fly through it...

The camera films the nature existing around them... Then he turns it back to the boys...

JAMES (CONT'D)
...while you sit at dinner with your captains and a hall made warm with a great fire...

Bill, seeing that he is becoming a little drowsy (but fighting it), firmly rescues the camera from his grasp.

JAMES (CONT'D)
So the life of man here appears for a little season... but what follows or what has gone before, that surely we do not know."

James swigs more morphine.

MILES
The Venerable Bede goes on to say that seeing as it's all unknown we should all be Christian. Live in fear of Hell.

James eyes Miles narrowly.

JAMES
I forget my audience. You're right. What a gamble it is - to have faith or pleasure. Faith! Or-

James passes out.

BILL
Thank Christ! Saved from the intellectual pissing contest.

CUT TO:

39 EXT. THE FERRY - DAY 39

The small ferry to the island, is moored with its engine running. The boys approach the shed on the quayside that serves as a ticket office. Above the booth a neon sign, strangely out of place, reads FERRY. In the shed is a TICKET MAN (gruff, scruffy 40), who looks at the boys and James in the cart with suspicion. James gets out and stretches. His leg is painful and he takes the weight off it. Only when the boys are closer do they see that despite the man's rough appearance he is wearing heavy eye make-up.

BILL
Hi there! We four, need to take the ferry... we and the cart.

TICKET MAN
When?

DAVY
Now, whenever you leave.

The man leans forward and silently counts them with minimal lip movements and nods. The boys are amused.

MILES
Four. There are four of us.

TICKET MAN
And the... cart?

MILES
Yes.

TICKET MAN
Single or return is it?

BILL
Return. But not today we're
camping.

TICKET MAN
Oh. (This appears to change
things)
When will you be coming back?

BILL
Monday.

The Ticket Man looks down at his tickets.

JAMES
(Quietly to Davy)
Is he wearing eye make up?

DAVY
He is.

TICKET MAN
All returns?

MILES
Yes! Does it run everyday?

The ticket man looks up at Miles wearily, as if this
questioning has interrupted his calculation.

TICKET MAN
365 days a year, 24/7. First
ferry at about 6 am last ferry
back at about 8 pm. No ferry
Christmas or New Year's Day or
Easter.

MILES
So it's neither 365 -

Davy sniggers and gets a sharp look form the ticket man.
James is pointing to a very faded notice in the window.

JAMES
It seems to say that a single
ticket is 3 quid... but a return
is 6.50.

TICKET MAN
Aye.

JAMES
Well why would anyone buy a
return?

TICKET MAN
For coming back.

JAMES
Do you sell many return tickets?

TICKET MAN
What's your problem, mate?

JAMES
Which one?

TICKET MAN
I'll have to charge you for the
cart.

BILL
What?!

TICKET MAN
Weight and volume. I'll charge
for an extra passenger? How does
that sound?

Bill steps forward angrily, but Davy pulls him back. The ticket man is smirking.

BILL
Alright! You're a criminal,
but... fine. Four singles and an
extra ticket for my terminally
ill friend's cart.

TICKET MAN
Single or return for the cart?

MILES
(Lunging back at him)
Listen, Tootsie-

CUT TO:

40 EXT. THE CHANNEL - DAY 40

The ferry pulls out for the short trip. Sun sparkling on the sea. Gulls flocking by.

CUT TO:

41 EXT. THE FERRY - DAY 41

Davy and Miles crouch down beside Bill - who has fallen asleep in seconds as usual - squeezing toothpaste on to his eyebrows.

James makes his way to the bow rail and looks across the water.

An old FERRYMAN leans on the rail nearby smoking a cigarette. James studies his profile.

FERRYMAN
(Without looking at James)
How long've you got?

JAMES
Not long. You?

FERRYMAN
(Laughs gruffly)
Same probably, boy... In pain?

JAMES
Yes.

FERRYMAN
Scared?

BEAT.

JAMES
Yes. (BEAT) I don't know. You?

FERRYMAN
Not really. But then... I'm old.

JAMES
Does that make a difference?

FERRYMAN
(He laughs a little)
Aye, I reckon it does.

James stares at him in silence for some time.

FERRYMAN (CONT'D)
History does anyway. By the time I got half way through my days I knew I was more afraid of killing than of being killed.

James thinks about this.

JAMES
Yes. I can see that would... I've had it very, very easy.

FERRYMAN
Not your fault.

JAMES
No. But I haven't really got started.

James looks over at Miles.

JAMES (CONT'D)
My friend's father died when we were sixteen; cancer. He was a writer. He was amazing. He was too young... but his books are still here... I haven't achieved anything.

The Ferryman does not respond.

JAMES (CONT'D)
I'm ready though, apart from that. Very little left to sort out.

FERRYMAN
Sort out? Sort out eh?

JAMES
Yes.

PAUSE.

FERRYMAN
If I said you had a beautiful body would you hold it against me?

JAMES
I'm sorry?

FERRYMAN
Song, by the Bellamy Brothers. Know it?

JAMES
Oh - Yes.

FERRYMAN
Did they mean hold your body close, or did they mean... take umbrage?

JAMES
I - I've never known-

The Ferryman shakes his head gravely.

FERRYMAN
But if the Bellamy Brothers got on this ferry, and they said, "It means both. That's why it's clever," so I finally knew, straight from the creators' mouth... So bloody what? Do you know what I mean?

James thinks hard.

JAMES
I don't think so.

The Ferryman grins devilishly.... James smiles.

FERRYMAN
Even when you have it all explained by the man himself. If you can't crack it... Can't see, really see why it's so smart... what's the point of being told.

James raises his eyebrows at the colloquial wisdom - looks round - hoping the others can hear... they can't.

JAMES
We're talking about dying aren't we?

The ferryman laughs until he chokes...

JAMES (CONT'D)
Have you... Can you say you've had a good life?

The ferryman looks at him for the first time, for a moment. Then he looks back at the water. He is silent for some time.

FERRYMAN
Yes. But then I've never asked much of it.

James looks back at the water.

DISSOLVE TO:

42 EXT. THE FERRY 42

As they cross the channel the boys are all lulled by the water and the motion. We see Davy watching James and looking pensive. Miles looking down, transfixed by the froth of the bow wave, and Bill sleeping peacefully with his toothpaste eyebrows.

CUT TO:

43 EXT. THE ISLAND. COAST PATH - DAY 43

The boys head up the coast and see the ferry heading back. James looks back at the small figure of the Ferryman who waves a farewell. James smiles a little.

CUT TO:

44 EXT. THE COAST PATH - DAY 44

James dozes in the cart. The other three talk quietly as they push it.

MILES
Thanks for the e-mail updates on the patient. My inbox is a nightmare. I always assumed they were pretty out of date by the time I opened them.

Davy nods, annoyed.

BILL
You're not looking for work?

DAVY
Not at the moment obviously.

Bill realises this was a stupid question.

MILES
Redundancy seems to suit you.

DAVY
Meaning?

MILES
Sorry. About an 8 on the tension scale there, Dave.

BILL
Ignore him. Jim's mum said you've been amazing these last few months.

DAVY
I just did what anyone would do. Well, I wanted to help and, I didn't get much redundancy pay but -

MILES
You going to go back to marketing - after this is over?

Davy grits his teeth in anger.

DAVY
What?

MILES
What?

DAVY
Is that a Miles-ism?... You think you're so clever and cute. It's exhausting.

MILES
I suppose I am sort of cute -

DAVY
Piss off -

Davy steps in a wet cow pat.

DAVY (CONT'D)
- Of course. Of fucking-course this is what happens to me now!

James wakes.

JAMES
Must've drifted off... (Looking about as if amazed) What have you bastards done to my room?

CUT TO:

45 EXT. CLIFF TOP - LUNCH SPOT 45

ANGLE ON: Davy, James and Miles stare at Bill blankly as he talks to them. (We only see Bill's head).

BILL
...and it turns out that Mengoll has been carrying the sword of truth, which is why it wouldn't kill Treeathor in the caverns. So they use it to destroy the orb and run out before the citadel explodes...

They stare at him blankly.

BILL (CONT'D)
It's not all worked out, but...

MILES
Put some fucking clothes on!

Only now do we see that Bill is totally naked again. Davy and James nod keenly.

DAVY
Do you even know how much you touched yourself at the bit about the witch? What's the matter with you!...

CUT TO:

46 EXT. THE COAST PATH 46

A montage of shots as the boys make their way onwards. It's exhausting, often having to lift the cart. It's starting to get more difficult for James.

CUT TO:

47 EXT. A FORK IN THE PATH 47

They study the map at a fork in the path...

CUT TO:

48 EXT. ROCK POOLS 48

The boys swap roles, pushing and pulling the cart. Through it we see James is becoming ever more uncomfortable and exhausted and the boys can see it.

They stop and James lies on the rocks. The others strip off to cool down in some rock pools and drink beer.

JAMES
A guy came to the door not long ago and asked if I was interested in winning a Caribbean holiday 'for those post Christmas blues.' I said I may well be dead by then. He said "Oh right - what about a luxury hamper?"

CUT TO:

49 EXT. TINY COVE - ROCKS 49

The boys are drying off and dressing. Davy comes over to where James is still lying. (We hear Miles and Bill in the background talking very seriously).

BILL
Honestly?

MILES
Yep.

Miles opens his back pack -looks for his clothes.

BILL
(Pointing at two invisible forms)
Jenna Jameson naked there.
Kristin Scott Thomas naked there.

MILES
(Nodding to the latter)
Double barrel all the way...

Davy comes over to get a towel from beside James.

JAMES
Davy - I can't get up. It's OK. It's just been a bit... more than I'm used to. Just need some meds. I'll be fine.

Davy helps him up and half carries him off the rocks.

JAMES (CONT'D)
Don't tell the others.

Davy nods, but looks worried and lifts him up, not noticed by Miles and Bill.

As he helps James to sit down by the pools, Miles is drying off and goes into his pack for fresh clothes, but they are missing.

MILES
Where the fuck are my clothes?

DAVY
What?

Davy goes through his pack.

DAVY (CONT'D)
Mine are missing too.

BILL
Yes. They are.

Davy and Miles stare at him.

BILL (CONT'D)
All your SPARE clothes are missing.

Davy is incredulous.

DAVY
Why? Why would you do this?

BILL
We should be living as nature intended us out here, with as few of the wasteful comforts as -

MILES
I'm going to fucking kill you.

BILL
We are going to experience this landscape...

Miles stalks towards Bill, who's laughing and backing away tripping over their half made camp. Miles leaps at him.

CUT TO:

50 EXT. FIRST NIGHT CAMP - NEAR THE TINY COVE 50

The boys are making camp. Bill is in overdrive.

BILL
This was a good choice Davy Gam.

James pokes at a fire sceptically wafting a pair of pants at it. Bill sees James's scepticism and shows him again the correct way to waft the pants at the fire.

BILL (CONT'D)
Waft! Waft!

Miles and Davy put up the second tent. This involves team work and though they are trying to do it amicably Davy yanks the tent too hard out of Miles' grip. Miles eyes him with annoyance. Davy pretends he hasn't noticed.

CUT TO:

51 EXT. FIRST NIGHT CAMP 51

The last of the seagulls skims the water on their way to roost.

The boys lie back after supper. Looking at the stars. Bill passes a joint to Miles who passes on to James, takes it.

BILL
Heaven.

Bill starts filming again.

JAMES
You know, if this were heaven, I'd be pretty chuffed.

MILES
I like the way you subtly brought it back round to you dying. I'd forgotten.

JAMES
Seriously. I don't believe in the pearly gates... What do you reckon?

James coughs. Davy isn't too happy about him smoking. James looks at Davy.

JAMES (CONT'D)
Come on!

DAVY
I don't know, I want to believe in something like God. I do.

BILL
Reincarnation... born again... as a...

JAMES
Mollusc.

BILL
(Smiling)
Don't piss on my nirvana!

Bill takes the boiling water and makes the tea, handing it out, relishing the ceremony of it. He LOVES tea.

JAMES
We don't think about our souls much... I've thought about little else since I first watched Anal Carnage 3...

This gets a hoots of encouragement from the boys.

JAMES (CONT'D)
Seriously, our souls... I don't bloody know of course... But I've read about it a lot and I'm pretty sure that it's all about the magical science that we barely know anything about. There's an idea in Buddhist faiths about a kind of constant energy... and quantum physicists have proven its existence... a perfect timeless universal space... It's just... "being", 'is-ness' - I can't help but see myself... in a million atoms of constant... sort of is-ness...

He has lost them but Miles stares at him surprisingly without cynicism.

JAMES (CONT'D)
(A little embarrassed)
I'm not explaining it very well.

DAVY
No. I think.... Yeah - I don't.

JAMES
Picture me tap dancing across the firmament and I'll be well satisfied!

Bill has a beetle on his hand and is watching it roam around his fingers, to distract himself. Davy looks terribly sad.

JAMES (CONT'D)
What about you Miles? What happens to you when you snuff it?

MILES
No idea.

JAMES
You must have thought about it.

This is too pointed. Miles shakes his head.

JAMES (CONT'D)
What's your instinct? I want to know!

MILES
After your 'dancing across the stars', you want to hear that I think there's nothing? That you're going to rot and that's it?

JAMES
Is that what you -

MILES
When my dad died, that's what I deci-

JAMES
Really?

MILES
Yes... How do you feel now - better or worse?

James swigs his morphine... There is a nasty, nasty silence. Bill is lost in thought.

BILL
I - Reincarnation's one thing, but one day we'll live on in our kids I suppose...

He looks up at James... This is no comfort to him.

CUT TO:

52 EXT. FIRST NIGHT CAMP. LATE 52

James looks at the sea and sneaks a secret swig of morphine. Then Bill goes to pass a joint to Davy, but James takes it.

BILL
(Laughs)
Christ this is a great cup of tea!

Bill takes more simmering water from the stove and adds it to his tea. Then he adds some more milk. He takes it and tastes it, and there is a trace of disappointment. James, coughing a little, watches this routine, laughs and shakes his head.

JAMES
You make a cup of tea and it gives you real pleasure! Then you ruin it. Why not finish it then get off your arse and make a whole new cup?

Bill laughs, but it seems James is angry.

JAMES (CONT'D)
Bill, you were going to film endangered tree frogs in the Amazon, save the planet... but you shoot a shitty quiz show, so you can pay the mortgage for a home you share with a girl who... I hardly recognise you. You're getting more and more watered down every day.

Long silence. Bill stares at his tea. He nods slowly.

MILES
Nice. Was that rehearsed or-

JAMES
Shut up, Miles.

BILL
He's right. I do do that. I just...
(MORE)

BILL (CONT'D)
I never seem to get things done the way I thought I would... And when I am happy... I just want... And now - Now -

They sit in silence watching Bill's agony. He tosses the ends of his tea away and shakes his head.

MILES
I love lessons learned through anecdotal observation. Seriously, did you prepare that or what?... ... And like you ever finish anything! I mean-

James is coughing badly and it hurts. Miles rolls his eyes.

Davy leaps up and frantically starts to get the meds out and seeing to James.

JAMES
It's fine.

DAVY
Shit! Are you feeling nauseous?

MILES
I am, but it's the tea-making-life metaphor.

James suddenly chokes on the mixture of morphine and pot.

DAVY
(In complete control)
Sit back. Take the Phemoryl. You'll be fine.

Miles and Bill look on helplessly. This is Davy's domain. Then Bill looks away. Miles looks at James and he's uncomfortable seeing his pain, so he gets up and walks to the edge of the cliff.

CUT TO:

53 EXT. CLIFF EDGE. 53

Miles tries to take a deep breath to control his rising anxiety. He can't. He tries, but he can't breathe... Slowly he manages to control it. After a moment he notices that Bill too has left James and Davy who are chatting (in the background throughout), and he joins him.

BILL
(Snapping out of his reverie and suddenly cheerful)
(MORE)

BILL (CONT'D)
We can get to Goat's Head
tomorrow easily. It's a great
spot. Soft grass, great view.

MILES
(With real tenderness)
Sounds good.

BILL
Miles, you know a lot about
women.

MILES
No.

BILL
My life right now is... I've been
with Abbie seven yea... And
sometimes it feels - Isn't this
what everyone feels after a
while?... I do love her... I do.

Miles looks at him.

MILES
Bill, we both know most people
settle for something that they
think is better than being alone.

BILL
Great! Is that me?

MILES
What? I don't know? How should I
know?

BILL
Why do I want the opinion of a
man who doesn't believe in love?

MILES
(Annoyed)
The love you're talking about is
like being an addict. You should
think 'I can't live without you
today'. You have to NEED that
woman's love coursing through
your veins. You'd stand in flames
to make her want you more! To
make her want you!

Bill looks back at Miles.

BILL
Mmmm - That's not me and Abbie.

MILES
Then do heroin. It's cheaper than women anyway.

Miles smiles. Bill looks at him.

BILL
Someone chink the armour?

MILES
No.

BILL
Ok... Do you always tell me the truth?

MILES
Yes.

BILL
Is there really such a thing as multiple orgasms?

MILES
Yes.

BILL
Damn it.

Davy comes between them. He is wears a pair of surgical gloves and a head-lamp. He holds up a very large white object like a GIANT pill (about 8cm long).

DAVY
(Gravely)
I have to get this up inside him...

He flicks on his head-lamp to illuminate the object in his gloved hand.

DAVY (CONT'D)
You guys will have to hold him down.

Miles and Bill look at it, then at Davy, in abject horror. Suddenly Davy collapses in hysterics. They hear James dissolve too. Miles and Bill sink with relief...

BILL
Bastards... God, it's soap... Very funny. I'm going to do it anyway! Teach you gaylords a lesson.

Miles and Bill leap on Davy.

FADE TO:

54 EXT. FIRST NIGHT CAMP. 5 AM 54

James wakes next to Davy. He reaches for some morphine and swigs as he clambers out of the tent.

He relishes strolling alone, across the countryside. Birds flit around him. The dew bejewels the cobwebs that blanket the plants. He drinks it in...

55 EXT. THE COAST PATH - EARLY MORNING 55

The sun gleams on the water. The boys have packed up. Miles and Davy push the cart away from where they camped. They all look a little more tired and dishevelled. Miles yawns. James is putting on a good show of being fine.

JAMES
See! Just needed some sleep!

MILES
Couldn't breathe in that tent. Bill's feet smell more like the wild than the wild.

Bill examines the tree that is now looking a little battered. He picks it up and runs to catch up.

MILES (CONT'D)
And no clean underpants thanks to the Wookie...

CUT TO:

56 EXT. FURTHER ALONG THE PATH -DAY 56

At one point on the path they have to lift the cart over rocks where the path has been washed away by the sea. James has to walk and relishes the challenge of it. Bill is proud, and loving it, but Davy looks really anxious.

CUT TO:

57 EXT. FURTHER ALONG THE PATH - A FARM GATE 57

Bill, Miles and James have crossed through a field full of cows. They are looking back at Davy who is on the other side refusing to walk through them.

DAVY
They're ALL staring at me now!

BILL
Come on!

Davy summons all his courage. He runs like a demented child through the cows. The boys laugh uncontrollably.

The boys cheer as Davy flies over the gate and lies panting on the grass. He opens his eyes and looks at the clouds. A smile spreads across his face and he starts to laugh.

CUT TO:

58 EXT. FIELDS. 58

Long shot. The boys appear over a hill together and determined.

They leave the path with Bill pointing towards a cluster of trees.

CUT TO:

59 EXT. FURTHER ALONG THE PATH 59

Amongst the trees at the top of a steep cliff. The boys are tired and look at each other doubtfully as Bill starts to climb down a rope.

BILL
We can't go round. This will save us a day that we just don't have.

A MONTAGE OF SHOTS:

As the boys lower James and the cart down the cliff on the rope.

Davy and Miles edge down beside James.

Suddenly the handle snaps on the cart. Davy and Miles can't hold it. James shoots down the slope on the cart. Bill braces himself as the cart hits him hard. He holds it.

DAVY
Jesus! You OK Jim?

JAMES
Fine...

MILES
Nice one Bill!

JAMES
Are we setting up camp soon?

BILL
Yes, mate.

DAVY
That could have been bad.

MILES
Oh Christ -

DAVY
Someone has to say it. Perhaps we can't -

JAMES
If it's me you're worried about - I'm fine.

DAVY
Maybe we shouldn't be going on too far-

MILES
We're not going back. We're going to Barafundle Bay.

BILL
It was a minor slip. As long as James wants to go on we go on... We gave our word and that's all there is.

James looks up at Davy.

JAMES
Every man's reach must exceed his grasp... else what's a heaven for!

Miles and Davy start pushing the cart. Davy stands there, thwarted but follows on. Bill turns to James and speaks with poetic gravity...

BILL
There once was a man called Nick,
Who was born with a corkscrew dick.
He spent his days in a life long hunt, To find a girl with corkscrew -

CUT TO:

60 EXT. TREES/CLIFF 60

The boys emerge from the tree line and are relieved to see the sea again. But the efforts of the cliff have taken their toll on all of them.

CUT TO:

61 EXT. THE CLIFF TOP. 61

The boys are sitting down. Bill has fallen asleep again.

JAMES
And you read the short stories?

James and Miles look at each other trying to keep their quizzical poker faces.

MILES
I e-mailed you, as you know.

James looks at Miles.

MILES (CONT'D)
The one about the bike-man, was great, really great... The one about the nurses was bollocks.

DAVY
I'm no writer, but I liked them.

Miles shoots a pointed look at Davy who returns it.

JAMES
There's no point pretending that I don't care what you think. I do, more than anyone -

Davy winces at this, though it's barely perceptible.

MILES
I'm not going to tell you they're good because -

JAMES
I'm a dying cripple.

DAVY
It's like you enjoy -

Suddenly Bill is up and on his feet.

BILL
(To Miles)
Miles - is that what you really thought?

MILES
Yes.

BILL
Cool. James - try harder.

This comes as a surprise to them all. But Bill already has his pack on and is moving on.

CUT TO:

62 EXT. GRASSY HILL. 62

The boys are all balanced at the top of hill and are all balanced on the cart.

DAVY
If the cart breaks-

BILL
How fucking dare you... Ready for take off...

JAMES
Take her steady Master Bates.

Bill gives a push with his foot and the cart starts down the hill slowly at first but gathering pace as the boys ride it. Bill whoops with the glory of it and even Davy joins in the triumph... But for James this speed is the most exhilarating and his face beams with joy.

CUT TO:

63 EXT. THE COAST PATH - THE GARBAGE COVE! 63

Davy, Miles and James sit where the path dips close to the level of a very narrow inlet. The inlet is knee deep in flotsam and jetsam. It's all industrial ocean rubbish. Multi-coloured plastic, canisters, packaging, rope, nets etc. As a whole this unnatural spectacle looks bizarre but almost like an artwork. Bill is down on the beach and he's talking to a strange figure in an old red cagoule with the hood up, and yellow waders. As they watch the pair start coming up towards them.

DAVY
(Sarcastically)
Great.

MILES
What do you think it is?

Bill scrambles up the low cliff followed by the BEACHCOMBER. He is about 40 and ruggedly handsome.

BILL
Guys! This is Jonathan Beaton. This is Miles, Davy, and that's James, our leader.

JAMES
The pleasure is ours. Shall I have Bill make some of his excellent tea?

BEACHCOMBER
Thank you, no. I have a flask of hot chocolate that I have to finish. I won't have tea until after my supper. Then I may have two mugs.

There is a slight pause as the boys take in this report.

BILL
This dude is amazing! Show them.

The Beachcomber reaches into the inside pocket of his cagoule and takes out a tiny orange bit of plastic the size of a toothpick. There is silence. The boys look at it. Then at the Beachcomber, then at it. Then at Bill who is beaming, then at it.

BILL (CONT'D)
He's looking for - You tell them!

The Beachcomber is coy, as if this is going to be the Lost Ark of the Covenant!

BEACHCOMBER
Darth Vaders.

Silence.

BILL
About a hundred thousand Darth Vader action figures!

DAVY
Star Wars toys?

BILL
From 1980!

MILES
(Quietly)
Is anyone else scared?

JAMES
I love where this is going.

The Beachcomber sits down.

BEACHCOMBER
Fifteen years ago I was in a bar in Marseilles. A Chinaman, speaking French, mentioned South Pembrokeshire.
(MORE)

BEACHCOMBER (CONT'D)
I was born here, so obviously I was interested. The Chinaman, a cargo boat skipper, was saying he'd lost a fortune. A container of Star Wars figures. But no ordinary Star Wars figures - faulty Darth Vaders - made brown like Ben Kenobi, instead of black. He reckoned they'd be collectors' items one day, so he decides to (*making bunny ears in the air*) "mislay" them... He leaves the docks at Milford, runs into a storm.

JAMES
An ungodly tempest.

BEACHCOMBER
No. A storm. His vessel is grounded, a man dies. The only container to go over, and break up on the rocks -

DAVY
Is -

BEACHCOMBER
Yes. Years later. I'm back here. Walking. Trying to clear my head - a lot - and I saw this cove. The wave approach and prevailing wind, make it the perfect filter. It should all be just beautiful drift wood, not this industrial flotsam and jetsam, but, you know, men should still wear hats every day, the world's changed!

The boys look at him blankly.

JAMES
Are you coming back to the Chinaman?

BEACHCOMBER
No. I realised this is where the brown Vaders would be, slowly washing up over the years. So I started looking. Every day I came down and looked. A month went by. Then two. Then three... nothing. I was starting to think I was crazy -

Miles and James exchange glances.

BEACHCOMBER (CONT'D)
Then one morning, spring of 2004 -

DAVY
NO!

BEACHCOMBER
No. I found a yogurt pot inside a sack of rubbish.

The boys stare blankly again.

MILES
(Under his breath)
Bagsy, I die first.

BEACHCOMBER
It had a 'sell by' date on it. November 1980. Proof that there was stuff washing up, from that exact year. Obviously I kept looking.

JAMES
Obviously.

BEACHCOMBER
A year, two years, three, four and still no brown Vaders. But I'm happily looking, seeing this beautiful view every morning, changing all the time, and then last month-

DAVY
NO!

BEACHCOMBER
No. But, I found this.

He holds up the tiny orange tooth pick like a treasure.

BEACHCOMBER (CONT'D)
It's a light saber from a Darth Vader made between 1980 and 1981.

DAVY
Wow!

BEACHCOMBER
Yep. They're here... If I find ten, they'll be worth thirty five thousand pounds. The container held more than hundred thousand. You do the math.

MILES
No.

James snorts trying to contain his laughter as he gets up. Davy jumps to help him.

DAVY
I never heard anything like it in my whole life!

JAMES
You speak for us all. I need a piss.

MILES
No! Let me. I'm dying to see his cock, it's been ages.

Miles follows James, but doesn't touch him. Davy looks irked that his job has been taken.

BILL
I'm going down there!

Bill leaps off the edge down to the cove.

NEARBY:

As Miles and Jim approach a suitable spot to pee at...

MILES
(Whispering)
Captain, we may have to sacrifice Nurse Davy to save ourselves.

BACK:

Davy is examining the light-saber. The Beachcomber is oblivious to the mirth he has caused.

BEACHCOMBER
Your friend is ill.

DAVY
Just excitable.

BEACHCOMBER
No the other one... Ja-

DAVY
I know I was joking. Yes, James. He's got cancer. Terminal.

Davy looks over at James and Miles.

BEACHCOMBER
Right. I lost a friend to cancer. My best friend ever.

DAVY
Sorry.

BEACHCOMBER
It's not your fault. It's just really really, really, really, really, really, really unlucky.

DAVY
(Wondering at his madness)
Right.

BEACHCOMBER
I have other friends. People find me attractive. But I started looking for a replacement for my dead friend. Among my existing friends, then acquaintances, and then new people.

LONG PAUSE.

BEACHCOMBER (CONT'D)
Why didn't you want the laughing-one to take your sick-friend to urinate?

DAVY
I - I didn't mind.

BEACHCOMBER
(Considering Davy)
Right.

DAVY
How long will you keep looking?

BEACHCOMBER
A friend? I don't anymore. That's the point.

DAVY
No, for the... (He gestures to the beach)

BEACHCOMBER
(Looking over to see what Davy's pointing at)
Oh that!... I took millions of photos of it all. That's what I used to do, you see. Fashion though. I put the photos in a book with some thoughts about stuff, rubbish mostly! Ha! And my agent in New York sold it, and it sold a lot, a lot, I mean A LOT!... So I'm OK. I'm more OK than ever... In fact I...

Long silence.

The Beachcomber seems to have realised that this is true for the first time in a long, long while. He and Davy look at each other. Davy smiles at him.

BEACHCOMBER (CONT'D)
Four years, haven't had to give a shit about anyone... Great to be needed isn't it? I'd forgotten.

Davy nods.

BEACHCOMBER (CONT'D)
You seem like one of the lucky ones. Satisfiable. That's rare. A gift. There already. And good. Well done.

Davy is totally bowled over considering this idea. James and Miles are back.

There is a silence.

BEACHCOMBER (CONT'D)
Sometimes I suddenly see things. Like when I take a picture. It's perfect. Right there... Click.

The boys watch him.

In the background we notice Bill tearing around the cove flinging rubbish about.

Suddenly the Beachcomber gets up, picks up his bag.

BEACHCOMBER (CONT'D)
Well - this was a life changing few minutes. James, we would have been good friends. Not best friends, but good friends. (He looks at Miles briefly, but says nothing. Then to Davy) You, I'm not sure. Good and possibly best. Yes.

DAVY
(Surprised)
Thank you. I - thank you.

BEACHCOMBER
No. Thank you.

Bill clambers up from the beach. The boys watch him go in bemused silence.

BILL
Good luck mate. Maybe I could come back sometime and help-

BEACHCOMBER
Nah. I'm done with all that shit. (He tosses the light saber into the cove) Enjoy your walk.

He strides off on a new mission.

BILL
I LOVE that dude!

DAVY
He was quite... I don't know he was actually -

MILES
I really thought he was going to kill us.

Davy helps James onto the cart while watching the Beachcomber.

JAMES
Possibly fuck us and eat us.

MILES
(Getting his pack on)
He could turn round of course. Stalk us until we settle down to sleep.

He gives a final wave and disappears, but Davy keeps watching. The others look at each other.

JAMES
David. Did that man try to touch your private place?

CUT TO:

64 EXT. SECOND NIGHT CAMP - EVENING 64

A delve on the cliffs beside a small rocky bay. The camp looks very inviting. Two tents have lanterns and the boys drink beers round the fire.

Miles and Bill set up fishing rods and lanterns on tripods in slapstick fashion in the background.

James takes some more morphine secretly while Davy's back is turned. Davy is checking his mobile phone secretly. Davy hurriedly re-packs it. Then Davy turns and sees James.

DAVY
You been hitting the morphine
kind of hard.

James looks at him. They both know he needed to. Davy feigns a smile and takes out the silver medication bag to do the other meds.

James takes this chance to reach into Davy's pack and steal his mobile and put it in his own on the cart.

Bill and Miles return to the fireside. Miles starts blowing up the pink lilo mattress.

BILL
We've done well. We could take it
easy and do another night.

Miles rolls over exhausted already.

MILES
No. I have to be in work on
Tuesday whatever.

James looks pissed off at this. Davy does too.

Bill lies down beside it and starts blowing.

DAVY
I still think we're carrying too
much.

Bill reaches out to the tree and hugs it to him.

DAVY (CONT'D)
The fireworks!

JAMES
Fireworks?

BILL
Davy!

JAMES
What fireworks?

BILL
You've ruined it!

DAVY
Sorry, sorry! But -

James is confused.

BILL
We had this idea, that because you love the stars, and having heard the whole 'dancing through cosmos' thing it seems doubly apt, that we try and... give them to you.

JAMES
Ha!

MILES
But they weigh a ton so let's just light the fuckers now.

DISSOLVE TO:

65 EXT. SECOND NIGHT CAMP - LATER 65

The sky is lit by an amazing shower of white cascading fireworks.

Miles and Bill set them off some way from the camp on the rocky cove. They are unsure of what they are doing.

At the camp we see James wrapped in blankets beside Davy. They watch with wonder.

DAVY
Am I annoying?

JAMES
Not now, mate.

DAVY
(Sad and guilty)
Sorry.

A firework explodes at the wrong angle. Bill and Miles shriek and dive out of its path.

James and Davy duck as it shoots over them and straight into one of the tents. The nylon tent bursts into flame.

As Miles and Bill arrive the tent has already evaporated and the kit inside is well alight as the firework continues to explode impressively. Davy grabs a small bottle of water and jumps about in panic splashing it onto the flames.

DAVY (CONT'D)
THAT'S FUCKING GREAT! WHAT DO WE DO NOW! YOU FUCKING IDIOT! YOU IDIOT!

MILES
It was him as well!

Bill soaks a towel and dampens the fire... and they manage to stamp out the rest.

BILL
That was an accident.

Most of the stuff inside has been burned, including their rucksacks. James has all but passed out from laughing and the pain it causes him. Davy, Bill and Miles stare at the wreckage exhausted and shocked. There is silence.

CUT TO:

66 EXT. SECOND NIGHT CAMP 66

The stars come out above them.

Miles is picking cautiously at a semi burned bag of crisps. Then Bill takes a deep breath and starts to sing -

BILL
"In this proud land I -"

MILES
No thank you!

Bill stops. James and Bill laugh. By torch and fire light Davy looks over the damaged kit. James watches them. Davy finds some condoms.

DAVY
Who packed these!?!

JAMES
Four straight guys, in the middle of nowhere, set fire to most of their stuff - but the CONDOMS are intact! Love it.

BILL
You can use them to cover a microphone actually. To record dolphins underwater. It's what they use.

DAVY
Cool. Everyone get that? It may not come up but - thanks Bill.

We shouldn't have cooked all the beans tonight.

BILL
We've plenty of food.

DAVY
I'm not worried about me!

MILES
Jesus, stop!

DAVY
Stop what! Stop making sure he gets to do this bloody trip! You two don't have any idea how much responsibility I have to shoulder so you can just piss around.

JAMES
You get thanks ALL the time.

DAVY
Well, that's nice -

JAMES
Davy, you're desperate to be needed.

DAVY
(Quietly to James only)
I'm glad you see it that way. I don't.

JAMES
I'm grateful!... But what ARE you going to do when I'm gone. I can't picture it.

DAVY
Who knows, Jim?

JAMES
But all you ever did was moan about being taken advantage of at work, until you lost your job, and I think my cancer came along at just at the right time.

Beat.

Davy's rage is simmering. But as usual he contains it.

MILES
I'll pay for all three of you to see a shrink when we get home. But for now -

JAMES
(Ignoring Miles)
It's not about failing it's about finding your...

MILES
Oh God. If you say 'raison d'etre' I'm killing myself.

JAMES
Shut up, Miles. This is -

MILES
Repugnant? Boring?

Bill clouts him on the head hard with a plastic bottle!

MILES (CONT'D)
Ow!

JAMES
Davy. Who the hell are you? What do YOU want? What perfect thing are you looking for?

BILL
James. I think he's doing fine. And you are being a bit -

MILES
There was no need to hit me.

JAMES
It's not what life's dealt you it's the cards you feel safe playing.

Davy is silent. His face is dead.

MILES
(Re: his head again)
You got me with the hard end bit, bro.

James looks at him, then at Davy, then at Miles. Drugs and pain wrack his body and his face has darkened to a storm.

MILES (CONT'D)
Well, I thought the tea making stuff was good - but -

JAMES
Miles, it's so fucking easy to take the piss, but I'm angry! With all of you!

MILES
(A sudden flash of anger)
Well you shouldn't be!

JAMES
WELL I AM!

Miles kicks himself for losing his temper even briefly as this will egg James on...

JAMES (CONT'D)
I don't want to die!

They are sobered.

JAMES (CONT'D)
I want more time. I want more time. I'd take any one of your pointless consumer-fucker lives!

James has tears in his eyes for the first time. Miles looks down and shakes his head.

JAMES (CONT'D)
I was going to do so much. I was going to be special. I know it sounds pompous. It is.

BILL
It is.

MILES
You are!

JAMES
I am! But... (to Miles) You make me sick.

Miles looks up to meet his stare.

MILES
Don't. I love my life. Cancer's no excuse for being such an egomaniac. Why are you special?

JAMES
You don't think I would have - (*become a writer?)*

MILES
I don't know! That's the point! By our age my father had written three novels already. (This wounds James.) Your writing's good, but you only sat down to finally do it because it got too difficult to stand up!

Miles looks to Bill and Davy. Davy is about to kill him.

MILES (CONT'D)
What? ...You want to hit me now, you pissy little arse-licker?

Beat.

DAVY
We're not your secretaries. We don't run away when you turn nasty.

MILES
I'm telling him the truth!

DAVY
Most people are blinded by the charm of The Great Miles. And you get away with being so -

MILES
You bore the fuck out of me.

DAVY
Why are you so cruel? Just cruel. There's other ways to get what you want.

MILES
(Nodding)
Wow! It's like you're actually looking at my soul through a microscope. (It becomes obvious he is taking the piss) I'm horrible - I have to find a way to redeem myself! Davy will you give me Aids!!!!!!!

Davy just stares at him. No one laughs.

MILES (CONT'D)
Bill? Rabies?

Bill wants to laugh but, James and Davy are still stony-faced. Miles shakes his head and backs away exasperated.

MILES (CONT'D)
God! GOD!

He gets up kicks a bottle of beer into the darkness...

MILES (CONT'D)
We don't NEED to do this! We don't! We should be laughing and talking bollocks about the old days...

Miles looks at James almost pleadingly...

JAMES
I read your novel.

Silence.

JAMES (CONT'D)
I read it. (Staring at Miles, but for the others to hear) He finished it years ago.

Miles walks away towards the fishing rods on the shore. James struggles to get up. Davy does not help. James takes a lantern and hobbles after Miles.

CUT TO:

67 EXT. SECOND NIGHT CAMP - SHORE LINE 67

Miles tries to calm himself, tries to breathe. He just wants one really deep breath.

James approaches with a lantern. He is in pain. Miles glances round. He really doesn't want to help, TO TOUCH HIM EVEN, so James lowers himself onto the sand.

JAMES
So, I read your book. Your lie can't exist.

MILES
When did you read it?

JAMES
Two years ago. I snooped on your computer. It seemed a natural part of the competition we'd been having all our lives. I found three drafts of the finished book... I copied the latest. I felt guilty and jealous. So I put it away. And I hated you for it. Then I got ill. And I gave in to my desire to... Even though I knew you'd never, ever forgive me.

MILES
I won't.

JAMES
It ruined me. You're right. Out of the two of us... you should - (*write.)*

MILES
I don't give a shit what you think of my book. I really don't. That book... means a lot to me -

JAMES
Because -

MILES
Oh, Shut up! Come on! You're going to tell me why it means a lot to me now?! Jesus this trip has been like a walk with the sick-white-Oprah! And you would hate you right now!

JAMES
Miles -

MILES
Mate, if you really need to tell me something you could have phoned me and I'd have come over. We would have had a chat and then we would have watched Jaws and pretended you weren't sick -

JAMES
I am.

MILES
Because you are! And when you're gone, when you're gone, you won't know how I... So all this is just unnecessary fake soul searching, that EVERYONE fucking does these days.

James tries to speak but Miles is off...

MILES (CONT'D)
I can't even say this REAL stuff, because I just may not get to see you again so I can -

JAMES
You don't have to apologise -

MILES
I wasn't going to apologise you arrogant little fucker! I'm right! And we never apologise!... I can say this shit, and see you in five minutes and say nothing! That's the point. There is one human... one other human being in this whole world, to who we can say anything. Anything. Anything.

JAMES
Your book is... You know it is.

MILES
Thank you.

JAMES
You're welcome.

MILES
I'm not afraid of failing now. I don't need to be -

JAMES
I know.

MILES
You see my Dad was so -

JAMES
I know.

MILES
(Nodding)
And now the only other person -

JAMES
Yes. I know.

MILES
Well, if you're not going to fucking listen.

James laughs raucously.

BACK NEAR THE TENT

BILL
It's the morphine talking. This morning he called me Robert.

Bill walks off towards James and Miles.

CUT TO:

68 EXT. SECOND NIGHT CAMP - LATER 68

Miles and Bill lie shivering by the dying fire.

BILL
I feel so honoured to be here.

MILES
I'd feel just as honoured to be with you all in a five star suite in the Caribbean.

BILL
I'm freezing.

MILES
Put your spare jumper on. No wait a minute...

BILL
So your book -

MILES
Shut up please.

CUT TO:

69 INT. THE TENT. 69

James lies awake. Davy faces away from him awake too. They talk quietly.

JAMES
Davy?

DAVY
What?

JAMES
What do you really think about what I said to you?

Beat. James is sipping secretly at his morphine.

DAVY
You've no right to talk to me like that. None.

JAMES
Why didn't you say that in front of them?

DAVY
(Coldly)
Loyalty you prick. Go to sleep.

CUT TO:

70 EXT. SECOND NIGHT CAMP 70

Bill shivers.

He gets up and creeps into the tent.

Miles suffers it a few moments longer then follows. We hear the groans and shuffling as they get into the tent.

BILL (V.O.)
(Whispering hoarsely)
Alright. I've got my knife. So any of you start getting 'Brokeback' I'll be going Rambo!

Beat.

MILES (V.O.)
Mmmm... God you feel warm.

DISSOLVE TO:

71 INT. THE TENT - LATER 71

The sounds of night by the sea. Inside the tent there are arms and legs everywhere. They look uncomfortable but each has an amusing slack-jawed expression. James is half awake, half asleep and lost in thoughts, and memories.

CUT TO:

72 EXT. A WIDE BEACH. 72

The four boys are younger. They are playing frisbee on the beach. They are laughing. In the dazzling sun we can make out James... young and healthy... life ahead...

CUT TO:

73 INT. A BEDROOM 73

The sun streams through a curtain in a foreign hotel room. On the bed lies a naked young woman. As the curtain floats in the breeze the sunlight plays across her hips...

CUT TO:

74 EXT. SECOND NIGHT CAMP - EARLY MORNING 74

The radio is playing. They pack up their kit. There's still a lingering tension between Davy and Miles. They side step each other as they pack away. No one has slept well. They look like insects unfurling in the sun.

Miles is struggling to get a tent peg out of the ground.

MILES
Shit it. Shitting thing!...I need-
Jim have you got that knife?

James tosses the old penknife from Davy at him.

He opens it and tries to pry the tent peg from the ground.

The blades snaps. He freezes. He looks up. They have all seen. James looks simply saddened by it - but Davy is livid. Silent but lived....

MILES (CONT'D)
Oh.

BILL
THAT was an accident as well.

CUT TO:

75 EXT. SECOND NIGHT CAMP 75

The cart is loaded. Miles holds it to stop it rolling down the slope. Bill and Davy bring stuff to put on it. Suddenly a phone rings. It's Miles' mobile.

JAMES
(Annoyed)
You promised!

MILES
It's work. I need to take this call. It's a very important situation -

BILL
More important than this trip?

MILES
Davy has a phone too!

DAVY
For emergencies! It's not about the phone. It's about you not really wanting to be here.

MILES
What?!

Davy snatches Miles' phone, which is still ringing, stops the call and sticks it in his pocket defiantly.

MILES (CONT'D)
Give me that phone.

The cart, that Miles was holding, is now trundling towards the cliff edge behind them. James sees it and shouts at them. They panic. Davy runs after it. Bill does too and falls over in hilarious fashion. But Davy runs towards the edge. He's almost at the cart as the cart reaches the brink. The cart sails over the edge. Miles is close behind and dives to catch Davy who would have gone over the cliff with the cart, and pulls him back!

DAVY
What are you doing?!!!

MILES
You would have gone over with it!

DAVY
I would have got it, you twat!

JAMES
He just saved your life.

BEAT.

MILES
You think he likes me more than
you, you whiny poof!

Davy takes Miles' mobile from his pocket and throws it over the cliff in rage.

Miles watches in disbelief.

Davy tries to look as though he doesn't regret it.

MILES (CONT'D)
Why do people keep throwing my
stuff in the sea?

Then he turns calmly to look at Davy. Bill steps in.

BILL
OK. That ALSO was an accident. We
can't afford many more. The
phone. That was bad. Bad, Davy.
But it's not the end of the
world. Miles your work knows
you've gone into the wild -

MILES
It's not that fucking simple.
It's all fucked! Things are bad.
People rely on me! The bank have
called in our loan. I'm going
under! (To Davy) Miles is
failing! You happy about that?

James looks down over the cliff again.

JAMES
Boys, we have a problem.

CUT TO:

76 EXT. CLIFF TOP 76

All the boys lie on the edge peering down at the cart, which rests broken on the rocks below. Miles rolls over onto his back and stares at the sky. James looks seriously ill.

DAVY
We'll call Mr G. Maybe they'll
send a helicopter.

JAMES
NO. No way... We haven't finished the walk.

DAVY
Mate, you weren't doing that much walking, and your transport is gone!

DAVY (CONT'D)
We'll call your dad. Maybe stay at a B & B on the mainland and he could find -

BILL
Where's your phone?

DAVY
In my bag.

JAMES
Uh. No. I'm afraid it's in my bag... on the cart.

There is a pause where they all compute this new problem. They look over the edge.

DAVY
This is un-fucking-believeable.

BILL
There's a kind of amazing natural symmetry -

DAVY
Shut up, Bill.

BILL
We've still got the tent. We'll just have to camp here while one of us goes back and gets help -

JAMES
(Lost in thought. Quietly)
No.

DAVY
Where's the map?

MILES
In the cart.

JAMES
We're going on. It's not far. I'll walk it. I can.

DAVY
James -

JAMES
No, Davy! I have to go on. I just want one night there. If you won't come I'll go without you. I have to. I have to.... I'm not finished!

He clambers to his feet and feebly heads off with fierce determination, despite being a shadow of the man that started the trip.

There is a moment of silent debate. They watch his tragic determined figure hobbling away. Davy looks at Bill.

BILL
We may be closer to the emergency phone at Barafundle - So... I could go back to the last phone. Reckon I can jog it in five hours maybe.

MILES
When did you last run for five hours?!

DAVY
If we go on we should stick together in case we have to carry him.

Davy glances at Miles but won't ask him.

BILL
What do you think Miles?

Miles is concerned, but he looks at James.

MILES
Thanks to you pricks, I doubt I'll have a company to go back to now.

They all look at James hobbling as fast as he can.

DAVY
Is it time to leave the tree -

BILL
(Abrupt)
The tree is one of us!

Davy rolls his eyes.

BILL (CONT'D)
So should I tell him or let him
keep going.

Davy shakes his head.

BILL (CONT'D)
James! Stop.

JAMES
Are you coming to Barafundle?

BILL
We are. But it's that way.

He points in the opposite direction.

FADE TO:

77 EXT. CLIFF TOP - MOMENTS LATER 77

Leaning on a stick and on Davy, James sets off gingerly.

Miles lingers behind and struggles to take a breath again.
He closes his eyes, calms down.

James looks ahead in agony.

CUT TO:

78 EXT. COAST PATH - LATER 78

James leans on Bill, but the pain is quite bad and fatigue consumes him. Though it is awkward on Bill's part, and James knows it. They silently change from James leaning as he walks, to leaning in more heavily... Bill takes more of his weight, having to put his arm round his waist, to James putting both arms round Bill's neck and eventually they come to a stop and Bill has to put down the tree. He offers his back. James clambers on without an ounce of energy to spare. Bill looks at the tree sadly. Davy hurries his step, and picks up the tree. Bill smiles at him. They walk on.

CUT TO:

79 EXT. THE COAST PATH 79

Exhausted, they have stopped for a break. Bill has fallen asleep with his back to the other three. Davy examines the gas can of the stove.

DAVY
Is this the only gas we have?
Bill?

MILES
Asleep.

JAMES
(Pain and drug addled)
Good to see him off the leash isn't it? Sooner he ditches that bitch the better.

MILES
How do you know that's what he wants?

JAMES
He's a big hearted, hilarious force of nature! And she crushes every natural urge he has. It's a horrible relationship. He has to face it!

MILES
It's none of our business. He's blissfully unhappy in his relationship probably, going through the ups and downs like everyone else.

James takes another swig of his syrup.

JAMES
People who are totally in love have arguments that burst the bubble only to facilitate the bubble's exquisite re-inflation.

Miles rolls his eyes. Bill slowly rolls over and gets up looking crestfallen.

BILL
"Facilitate the bubble's exquisite re-inflation." Hmm. Not me and Abbie.

Awkward silence. There is a silence that is finally broken by James.

JAMES
Thank God! Bill, make a clean break.

MILES
Be vile and distant 'til she cheats on you.

JAMES
This is a new start -

BILL
Abbie's pregnant.

There is a dreadful silence.

James is particularly filled with horror and confusion.

This was not in his plan.

Bill looks darkly at the ground.

JAMES
Why didn't you say?

BILL
I wanted to enjoy the walk.

JAMES
Congrat-

BILL
Don't.

Pause.

DAVY
I'm not saying it's good news, in the circumstances, but you'll be a brill-

MILES
Definitely yours?

Bill is aghast at this but thinks about it...

BILL
Far as I know.

DAVY
Baby or not... if she isn't the one -

BILL
Of course she isn't the fucking one!

JAMES
Well then, grasp - (*the life YOU want.*)

BILL
(Angry)
It's not that simple.

JAMES
But -

BILL
(ANGRY. ANGRY. ANGRY)
Shut the fuck up, Jim! Yeah it all gets "watered down"! It does. With every year. But I know that what I do with my life affects other people. I stick to my decisions - however shit - I'm trying... I may not set the world on fire, but I see things through! And when all my dreams come to nothing, I'll be around to fucking see it!

Beat.

BILL (CONT'D)
(To James, then Miles and Davy)
You should have told me before! You should have told me!

Bill backs away from them shaking with rage.

He stumbles over the tree. He grabs it. He brandishes it above his head like a mace and pounds it on the ground. Then picks it up and does it again. Now he swings it round twice and sends it flying over the cliff... He watches it disappear...

The boys just stare at him.

Bill's rage subsides. He slumps to his knees on the cliff edge, totally spent, looking at the sea.

The boys look at each other. Eventually... Miles walks over to Bill and stands facing the sea, but very close to him.

MILES
Well... You really showed that tree.

Bill laughs. The tension is released and he leans against Miles' leg. Miles roughs his hair, as though patting a much loved old dog that has just failed to catch a rabbit.

CUT TO:

80 EXT. COAST PATH. 80

The boys are tired and struggling. Davy and Bill carry heavy packs. Davy carries James on his back.

They have stopped to rest. James is suffering. Bill sits a little apart and nurses serious blisters... but without dressings for them he just pulls his boot on in agony.

They all look at each other. They all know going a step further may be beyond them all.

James tries to walk on. He looks out at the sea. He watches a cormorant that is hovering at his eye-line dive into the sea. He looks at the birds and smiles.

BILL
I'm sorry about your tree. I'm going to grow another. We can -

JAMES
Do you know what? I wouldn't have it any other way... My tree will drift... wash up on some strange shore.... perfect.

Bill smiles.

CUT TO:

80 a EXT. CLIFF TOP. DAY. 80 a

Bill, Miles and Davy follow, carrying their kit. But, unnoticed by Davy, his pack, which has a hole burnt in it from the fire, starts to tear apart as he walks and pieces of kit drop out.

No one is talking. Each in his own private miserable world, they concentrate on nothing but moving forward.

Further along Davy is carrying an exhausted James. Bill is carrying Davy's pack. Even he is just trudging on step by step now, limping badly but trudging on with gritted teeth.

Miles is at the rear looking scared.

Pull out to show the great distance of wilderness ahead...

CUT TO:

81 EXT. THE COAST PATH 81

They get to a steep rise and stand at the bottom.

James is on Bill's back.

He adjusts his hold on James and starts to climb.

Bill stumbles. Davy and Miles leap forward to try and catch James and Bill but too late and Bill falls. His efforts to protect James cause him to fall badly and James cries out in pain. Bill and Miles just look at him. Helpless, but Davy grips James hand.

DAVY
You're alright! Breathe in.

James is pulling on Davy's hair.

Miles is appalled.

MILES.
Right. Are we done? I mean I think we're done now. Fuck it. I'll run back. Bill runs on, or vice versa. One of us will get there. We might see a boat or -

DAVY
Shut up Miles. We'll be fine.

James focuses on Davy's eyes. He smiles as much as he can manage.

MILES
Bill? This is fucking mental!

Bill looks at Davy.

BILL
I don't know.

Davy laughs.

MILES
Jesus!

DAVY
(to Miles)
You carry Jim for a bit.

Miles looks scared. He looks at James who is paler than ever. Miles looks up the steep incline ahead and back at Davy.

MILES
Don't tell me what to do -

DAVY
Why?

MILES
You feeling all hard now?! Why? Because I didn't kick your arse for chucking my phone away... or because I'm -

DAVY
Oh - just shut it! This isn't about you right now. Pick him up!

MILES

No.

DAVY

Pick him up.

MILES

Fuck you!

DAVY

Pick him up, you fucking coward!!

Miles swings at him and lands a punch on the top of Davy's head, which hurts his hand.

Davy swings back and soon they are rolling on the floor trying to kill each other.

Bill watches shaking his head. James turns from the cliff edge to look at them. Miles and Davy fight with neither obviously winning.

JAMES

We should stop them.

BILL

Well... I know we should... but it's kind of fascinating...

Davy and Miles both give up at the same time totally exhausted. They fall back.

BILL (CONT'D)

Let's call it a draw... (To Miles) I liked the little 'EEEK!' noise you made when he got you in a head lock.

Miles looks at him and then can't help laughing. Neither can Davy.

There is a silence.

DAVY

We're men now! And it turns out I'm a pretty fucking average man! And you know what - Heaven forbid that I should learn anything on this fucking trip... But I have! I've got people who love me. People I love back. And I'm happy. This is all there is and it hurts and it's amazing. But it's the truth. But I'm not afraid of it... and THAT is what makes you suddenly despise me.

Miles is beaten. Davy stares at him waiting for the attack but sensing victory.

MILES
It is easier winding you up than saying it all and being... well, - You.

Miles and Davy grip hands in conciliation.

BILL
This trip is awesome.

MILES
(Weakened beyond recognition. Looks to James)
Your illness disgusts me. If I got sick like that, I'd be so totally humiliated. It shocks me. That's ALSO the truth. After my Dad - I actually don't need to say this. I don't have to.. But I am - SO sorry.

Miles gets up and goes over to James and starts to heave him up and onto his back. Davy and Bill help.

MILES (CONT'D)
Come on, you bugger.

He starts to climb the massive incline.

It's tough, this is a huge challenge... it's painful for James and Miles is struggling to climb at all.

CLOSE in on: Miles and James. They are silent. Both in pain of different kinds.

PAUSE. Gradually the action slows to slow motion. We hear two different heart beats. One stronger than the other.

Finally, with Bill and Davy supporting Miles and James, they reach the summit and collapse again.

CUT TO:

82 EXT. BARAFUNDLE BAY 82

From the summit of the hill they see Barafundle Bay.

The sun kisses the water at a million glistening lips.

They stare at the cove for a moment taking it in.

BILL
Barafundle Bay. Jesus.

DAVY
Told you we'd make it.

They laugh.

BILL
I'd forgotten how incredible...

JAMES
Yeah... this isn't actually the
one I was thinking of.

They laugh.

JAMES (CONT'D)
Thank you.

They are thrilled. They make their way down to the beach.

CUT TO:

83 EXT. BARAFUNDLE BAY -THE BEACH 83

The boys have dumped their bags and run into the water, leaping about in the surf. Even James is in knee deep, watching his friends with affection.

CUT TO:

84 EXT. THIRD NIGHT CAMP - BARAFUNDLE BAY - LATER 84

Still a little wet from the swim they have started to set up camp and Bill has a fire going. They are happy. But across the laughter James and Miles make eye contact. There is the hint of suspicion in both their eyes. James raises his morphine syrup in a toast to him.

Miles nods.

The laughter continues and their eyes are diverted by the chatter.

CUT TO:

84 b EXT. THIRD NIGHT CAMP - MOMENTS LATER 84 b

James is dozing. The other three have gathered driftwood to make shelters around the fire, tying them with bits of rope from the flotsam and jetsam. As they work:

DAVY
...Waste of money. Hated going to
the gym anyway. Full of Russian
gangsters -

MILES
You haven't spent all your redundancy already have you?

DAVY
No -

MILES
Only. It's tough out there at the moment -

DAVY
No. I don't need -

MILES
I could have helped but, now -

DAVY
It's fine. But thank -

MILES
Do you have a little nest egg to -

'Course you should put into property. But -

DAVY
Maybe I can get my old job -

MILES
Well, like I say, if I can throw something your -

BILL
Wait. Davy, 'get your old job back'? I thought you were made redundant? You can't.

Miles realises what Davy has said and both he and Bill look at him.

DAVY
Yeah. I, um...

BILL
You quit for this didn't you.

Davy doesn't answer. They are silenced.

Eventually Bill slaps him on the back and keeps working on the driftwood shelter.

So does Miles. But as he works...

MILES
You're a class act Davy. A class act.

With only a sideways glance to each other they on with their jobs, but this has meant the world to Davy.

CUT TO:

85 EXT. THIRD NIGHT CAMP - BARAFUNDLE BAY. BEACH - EVENING 85

The camp is more established. Bill has fashioned driftwood into sculptures around the camp that act as a wind break and throw strange shadows in the flickering firelight. James watches them.

BILL
Is there anything so peaceful as the sound of the ocean?

JAMES
Bill. Whatever the circumstances... any child will be so lucky -

Bill nods...

Only Miles looks away. He looks unhappy.

JAMES (CONT'D)
Fuck. Sorry guys. I was so proud of myself for my stoicism. I thought I could wrap everything up neatly... and then -

MILES
I'm fucking your sister.

James just stares at him. Miles stares with a strange look of calm danger in his eyes that antagonises and inspires.

James nods slowly and looks to the sea. This is not what Miles expects. He looks to a stunned Bill and Davy.

Eventually James looks back at him impassively.

MILES (CONT'D)
I am totally and utterly in love with her and I have been for ten years.

JAMES
(Genuinely surprised now)
Shit.

MILES
I watched her marry Mike and did nothing. Have children, settle down in her big comfortable life....
(MORE)

MILES (CONT'D)
Only then did I really know I had to find... I pursued her. And I got her.

JAMES
My God.

MILES
We met up in when you got sick and - well... Ironic isn't... Terribly ironic.

JAMES
Yes.

MILES
I'm going to buy a big house and one day, soon, she'll leave Mike. Then, sometime after, she'll bring the girls to my house... and she'll be mine.

Beat.

JAMES
I always knew she had a thing for you but, most women seem to -

MILES
NO. No. I wanted her. She would never have... I wanted her. So I took her. And we are perfect for each other. Perfect in every way. Perfect. Perfect.

JAMES
Jesus! I mean it'll...

James, Davy and Bill stare at Miles mentally envisaging all the stress and turmoil this will cause to all involved, after James is gone... Miles just stares back at James.

JAMES (CONT'D)
When were you going to tell me - Oh. You weren't.

MILES
No.

JAMES
So, do you want my blessing?

MILES
No. I'll do it anyway.

PAUSE

JAMES
Yep.

MILES
Yep.

They sit in silence.

MILES (CONT'D)
My father always told me that one thing is bigger and better and stronger than everything and everyone in this world put together. I'd ask him what it was and he would never tell me. He said I'd find out if I were any son of his. I...

JAMES
I do so hope it turns out well.

Silence.

BILL
So do I.

Miles looks at Davy who stares at the fire.

DAVY
It makes sense. Weirdly, it makes sense.

Miles is surprised by Davy's gravity. Humbled.

They sit in silence for a while again. James gets up, slowly. Davy and Bill go to help him but he waves them away.

He walks to the edge of the sea and watches as the last birds head to roost.

He is lost in thought for a while.

Suddenly Miles is beside him.

MILES
I know what you wanted.

JAMES
There is no ribbon to tie around it all is there?

He looks at Miles, who just stares at him.

JAMES (CONT'D)
I thought I was ready... Now I look at Bill and wonder if I could just get through another nine months. And if I could hold on until Chloe is sorted with or without...

James stares at the sea. He nods slowly.

JAMES (CONT'D)
I'm leaving early. And it all goes on without me.

MILES
I'm so sorry.

James whips round to look at him.

JAMES
Strange thing is - this is what I was most afraid of. But now it's a relief, Milo. It's such a bloody relief.

Miles nods... James struggles to get up. Miles helps him. James walks back to the tent and the fire needing to lean on Miles. They sit and are all silent.

JAMES (CONT'D)
I'm going to go for a swim.

Davy and Bill look at him but Miles' head drops.

DAVY
Your mum said you -

JAMES
I know. Tomorrow, I'm going to swim out into the bay, and I'm not coming back. I know the enormity of this, but I'm asking you to let me swim.

Bill and Davy stare at him in horrified silence. Miles' head sinks further and he stares at the sand.

DAVY
No.

BILL
Jim, we just can't do that. Why -

JAMES
You can. The question is will you?

BILL
Has this been your plan all along?

James nods.

BILL (CONT'D)
I thought you wanted to live. Why -

JAMES
(Gesturing to himself and the effect the walk has had)
Because this is what my life is going be like! Because of the pain, and the drugs I take for the pain, and the drugs I take for the side-effects of the other drugs... You've seen it. And it's only going to get worse. Life is all up here really, but it takes over. Gradually I'll slip further into thinking solely about pain. And that's not worth living for.

BILL
I don't know what the pain's like but surely we can...

JAMES
What?

BILL
I don't know. I just... We can't let you swim, mate.

JAMES
Stop saying you CAN'T. You can. But you won't.

James looks at Miles - silently, calmly watching.

BILL
What would we say to your mum and dad -

DAVY
This is crazy! I can't even believe you're talking about it normally!

JAMES
The same as you'd say to the police. That when you woke up I'd gone. You checked the dunes and then you saw something floating in the water.
(MORE)

JAMES (CONT'D)
That you came to get me but it was too late. (Beat) One of you had run up to the headland to the emergency phone. You wouldn't be alone for long.

BILL
But every time I looked at your family I'd know they could have had you for another day. Said goodbye properly...

JAMES
That's just it, there won't be a better goodbye than the one we had.

DAVY
There will! It's not time yet.

JAMES
I've never been so alive. And now I want to end it, to actually finish something!

BILL
Why don't you just go home and take an overdose like normal people.

James laughs.

BILL (CONT'D)
It'd be painless. You'd just fall asleep.

JAMES
I'd be quitting. If I swim out and the sea takes me, it's different... I'd be making the choice! I want to be conscious until I'm gone, I want to feel something even if it's the pain of salt water in my lungs... I want to feel the fight. Something huge and terrifying and brave.

DAVY
I promised your mum I'd bring you back.

BILL
Sorry James.

Heartbroken, James looks at Miles.

Miles shakes his head.

JAMES
OK. OK. It was too much to ask.

SILENCE. James nods slowly then grimaces in pain.

Davy jumps up and goes to the tent. The others sit staring into the flame. James shivers and grimaces a bit, shifting in discomfort. Davy emerges from the tent with his pack. There's the big burn hole in it.

DAVY
I had the silver bag - it must have dropped out.

They rummage through their bags. There's no silver bag.

DAVY (CONT'D)
He doesn't have any morphine.

JAMES
I'm not deaf.

BILL
We'll find it. Miles?

James looks really worried for the first time. Miles looks terrified.

James nods. He's in pain. Davy tries to make James comfortable as Bill and Miles jog back up the path scanning the ground with their torches.

CUT TO:

86 EXT. COAST PATH. NIGHT 86

Inter-cut scenes of Miles and Bill running and searching in the dark for the silver med-kit, with:

CUT TO:

87 EXT. THIRD NIGHT CAMP - CAMP. NIGHT 87

James gets progressively more and more sick and his pain increases. Davy helps him into the tent. And wraps him in the sleeping bags. Moving into the tent causes him to cry out in pain and the sound carries across the headlands...

CUT TO:

88 EXT. COAST PATH. NIGHT 88

The beams of Miles' and Bill's torches scan the ground and they can hear the distant sound of James crying out. They go on looking frantically.

CUT TO:

89 EXT/INT. THIRD NIGHT CAMP - CAMP. NIGHT 89

James writhes in agony, delirious, crying out to try and control it.

[Inter-cut with the coast path where the torch light beams scan the ground. James' voice echoing through the darkness. Short of breath. Talking incredibly fast, almost indecipherable.]

JAMES
Oh God!... Enough! I can't...
God! If you can hear me! Please!
GOD! Fuck you! Help me!

90 EXT. COAST PATH. NIGHT 90

The torch beams scan the ground. Miles and Bill run on.

JAMES (V.O.)
If there's nothing... if there's nothing... It's less than an instant... God! God! If there's nothing...

Suddenly the beam of Bill's torch falls on the silver bag containing the meds. He weeps with relief.

BILL
I've got it! I've got it!

The boys run back and still they hear James calling out, getting louder and louder as they approach.

CUT TO:

91 EXT. THIRD NIGHT CAMP - NIGHT 91

Davy rips the meds bag open and takes out a bottle of syrup and helps James to drink it.... It quickly starts to take effect as Davy takes a morphine 'patch' and sticks it on James' arm. James is still shivering and wracked but his breathing slows a little... a quiet descends... Bill and Miles collapse by the fire with relief but don't talk. By firelight we see they have been traumatised.

DISSOLVE TO:

92 INT. THE TENT. MIDDLE OF THE NIGHT 92

Davy is fast asleep. Alone in the tent. Miles leans over him and wakes him gently. He wakes with a start sensing immediately that James has gone.

DAVY
(Whispering)
Where is he?

MILES
He's fine. Come and listen.

CUT TO:

93 EXT. MIDDLE OF THE NIGHT 93

Miles leads Davy silently to the headland nearby where Bill stands, his arms supporting James, wrapped in a sleeping bag, who looks terribly ill. They look out into the moonlit bay... The air is filled with the sound of whale song and soft puffing as they break the surface of the still water to breath. The boys look at each other and smile but say nothing.

DISSOLVE TO:

94 EXT. NIGHT THREE CAMP - DAWN 94

The grey light finds Miles and Davy and Bill still by the fire, awake and looking ravaged by the night's experience. Bill pokes at the embers and manages to get a flame again. Miles, looks from the sea to Bill. They stare at each other for a while. Davy notices their look. Miles nods at Bill slowly then looks back at the sea. Bill looks at Davy, then back at the fire.

James is now at the shoreline, sitting alone, wrapped in his sleeping bag. The sparkling sea laps at the shore. The boys watch him. James gets slowly up and turns to look at them. He smiles.

Bill gets up, tears in his eyes and walks over to him.

JAMES
I get the feeling we'll meet again?

BILL
We're all just dust dancing in the flickerlight...

JAMES
Good luck, Bill.

Bill beams but a tear rolls down his cheek. James laughs warmly.

BILL
I'm shaking... I can't stop.

JAMES
Bill. Bill!... You're a giant!
There are so few left.

James hugs him.

Davy comes to them. He is in shock.

DAVY
I can't do it... You can't do it.
How -

JAMES
It's just tough. But you said it.
It's amazing. Look around us.
It's so worth it.

James hugs him. But Davy can't look at him.

JAMES (CONT'D)
I envy the people that you will love.

James turns to Miles.

JAMES (CONT'D)
Mate.

MILES
(Nodding)
Yep.

JAMES
Thank you.

They smile at each other. But their smiles fade slowly together. They look young and scared.

MILES
Go on if you're going.

James' fear is gone suddenly. He smiles and turns to the sea. He walks in gingerly, it's cold, he is breathing hard.

JAMES
You could catch your death in here!

He goes in and swims a bit in the shallows. The cold takes his breath. He laughs... On the beach the boys look on in horror, Davy cries, shaking his head.

James looks at them then he turns around and starts to slowly swim out. He looks back once more and then swims on.

Miles takes off his shoes, and checks his pockets. He takes out some coins and with them the white feather. He looks at and tosses it away. Then he strides in to the water.

Bill follows and lastly Davy, though he's not sure if this is a rescue or not. It's not.

Miles catches up with James and swims near him. Bill is on the other side. Davy, the weakest swimmer, is behind. James looks at them, glad they are there. They swim in silence.

Davy is upset and accidentally swallows water and chokes. Suddenly he's struggling. Bill, Miles and James look at each other... there is something absurd about this. But Davy is in real difficulty and panics as he starts to go under, coughing and spluttering. Bill goes to his rescue. Bill struggles to hold him and takes him back to the beach. James and Miles watch the rescue with bewilderment.

MILES
Fuck. You nearly out-lived Davy!

James laughs and then gets a spasm of pain and he can't stay afloat. Miles drags James towards him.

James' nerve recovers and he pushes himself free. James treads water. They stare at each other for a few moments.

ON THE BEACH:

Davy tries to run into the water again, but Bill holds him back. Davy struggles to get away but Bill holds him firmly. Davy collapses on the sand. They watch helplessly.

IN THE WATER:

James is exhausted. He struggles then lets himself go under. Miles is unsure what to do. He looks to the shore and sees Bill and Davy. Then he looks at the bubbles rising. Silence. Suddenly James bursts from the still surface, gasping, reaching for Miles... Miles holds him. They stare at each other for a moment... then they laugh.

But the laughter fades...

MILES (CONT'D)
You've ruined this camping trip.
Can we go home now?

James shakes his head sadly.

JAMES
Sorry. If you can't do it. Tell
me. I'll swim as far as I can...
I'd rather not be alone, mate.

MILES
Jim. Jesus Christ, Jim. I act like I'm special, but it's fake... Jamie... It's fake. I'm scared. Of everything. There's no one to look after me.

Miles can hardly breath. James stares at him and realises that he can't do it. And the disappointment is crushing.

JAMES
Please Miles. Do this, this... dreadful, wonderful thing for me.

Tears run down James' face. James takes a deep breath. He's shaking and he can't stay afloat.

JAMES (CONT'D)
Miles!

Miles holds him. They stare at each other. Miles nods almost imperceptibly. This is the end. James is weak and beaten and tired. He looks around at Bill and Davy. He looks at the sea, and the sky... and smiles... he looks relieved.

JAMES (CONT'D)
It's all so....

He looks at Miles. Miles still stares at him, he is petrified. James sees it. They keep fierce eye contact.

JAMES (CONT'D)
(Whispering)
...We are the makers of dreams, and this little life...

MILES
That was the last thing my father said -

JAMES
I know. I read your book.

Miles nods almost imperceptibly. Miles holds him by the shoulders and they stare at each other.

JAMES (CONT'D)
God speed.

James allows himself to sink under the water.

Miles can hardly breathe. He stares down.

James stares up at him. Now Miles sinks with him.

He holds James under.

James' breath runs out, and he starts an involuntary convulsion. His face shows the fear and panic and he grabs at Miles' face fighting to save himself - to swim to the surface - but Miles holds him under. Miles fights himself with all his will-power to hold him down. His own breath is running out. The urge to lift James from the water is unbearable. Their eyes never leave each other. Miles can't hold on much longer... Then suddenly James goes limp. He's still alive - staring. Miles has no need to hold him down now. The water has filled James' lungs. The bubbles of air have gone. He sinks. There is stillness. James sees the blue sky behind Miles, the sun light flickering on the surface of the sea behind Miles, making him seem to glow.

FINALLY - Miles kicks to the surface. Alone.

He takes great gasps of air. His lungs finally fill. He is breathing. He is alive.

James is still under the surface. Miles stares into his face. James is dead.

Miles drags James' body towards the shore. Waist deep in the water he stands there. He doesn't move for a few moments, unable to believe that James is really gone. He tries to carry the body but he falls.

Davy rushes into the water first to Miles and hugs him.

He looks him in the eyes and hugs him again.

Then he looks at James and reaches under the water to touch him. Davy, Bill and Miles drag James from the water and on to the beach.

Bill, shaking, looks between Davy and Miles. Miles is lost in his own world. He slumps down staring at the sea too.

Davy stares down at James and reaches out to touch his hair but suddenly he stops.

DAVY

He's gone... This isn't him.

Davy arranges James body into a more 'comfortable position'.

He goes to the tent and gets a large towel and drapes it around Miles' shoulders. It is brilliantly white in the morning sun.

Davy looks at Bill and Miles and then at James. Then he runs away towards the steps up from the beach.

CUT TO:

95 EXT. JAMES' HOUSE 95

A police man and a policewoman walk towards the house. Chloe crosses the garden from the orchard with a bucket of apples. She sees them. She drops the apples. She stands motionless for a few seconds then she starts to pick up the apples quite calmly. She stops looks at the sky... then carries on picking up the apples.

CUT TO:

96 INT. JAMES' HOUSE. 96

The party scene as at the beginning. Slow motion. James is bending down towards the candles. His happy face illuminated by their flame of 29 candles.

JAMES (V.O.)
I'll raise a morphine syrup to you later, while I'm selling your presents on e-bay. And if over the years you should happen to notice that it's the anniversary of my birth remember that you were loved by me, and that you made my life a happy one... and there is no tragedy in that.

He takes a huge breath and... blows out the candles.

CUT TO:

97 EXT. BARAFUNDLE BAY 97

Davy comes running down the beach out of breath, but focussed. The other two don't look at him. He looks at his watch. He sits on the beach beside Miles.

They look at all the sky. At all the sparkling water.

FADE TO BLACK.

98 CAPTION: 98

James Kimberly Griffith

1979 - 2010

Accidental death by drowning.

FADE TO BLACK:

Amidst the black, a firmament of twinkling stars appears.

JAMES (V.O.)
Listen, the thing about life is... What? (HE GIGGLES AGAIN.) Oh bollocks! We'll start again later... (HE LAUGHS LONG AND HARD)

The laughter trails away... And for a moment there is nothing but the universe then...

FADE OUT.

Cast and Credits List

Director :	**Hattie Dalton**
Writer :	**Vaughan Sivell**

Cast

Davy :	**Tom Burke**
James :	**Benedict Cumberbatch**
Miles :	**JJ Feild**
Bill :	**Adam Robertson**
Beachcomber :	**Hugh Bonneville**
Mr. :	**Rupert Frazer**
Mrs. :	**Helen Griffin**
Ticket Seller :	**Karl Johnson**
Chloe :	**Nia Roberts**
Angel Boy :	**Eros Vlahos**

Producer :	**Kelly Broad**
Executive producer :	**Pauline Burt**
Executive producer :	**Kate Crowther**
Line producer :	**Kate Dain**
Executive producer :	**Margaret Matheson**
Associate producer :	**Adam Robertson**
Producer :	**Vaughan Sivell**
Executive producer :	**Nigel Thomas**
Executive producer :	**Charlotte Walls**

Music by :	**Stephen Hilton**
Cinematography :	**Carlos Catalán**
Film Editing :	**Peter Christelis**
Casting :	**Catherine Willis**
Production Design :	**Richard Campling**
Art Direction :	**Johnny Campling**
Costume Design :	**Marianne Agertoft**
Hair & make-up designer :	**Jo Evans**
Production manager :	**Tom Jenkins**

PRODUCTION OFFICE
MANOR HOUSE
THE OLD FARM YARD
STACKPOLE ESTATE
PEMBROKE
SA71 5DQ
Tel

USEFUL MOBILES
Producer: Vaughan Sivell 07*********)
Producer: Kelly Broad 07*********)
Line Producer: Kate Dain 07*********)
Production Manager: Tom Jenkins 07*********)
2nd Assistant Director: Christian Rigg 07*********)
Coordinator: Sukey Richardson 07*********)

BARAFUNDLE BAY

CALLSHEET # 1 THURSDAY 17th SEPTEMBER 2009

DIRECTOR: Hattie Dalton PRODUCER: Kelly Broad PRODUCER: Vaughan Sivell	**ON CAMERA: 0800** B'FAST @ UNIT BASE FROM : 0715 LUNCH @ UNIT BASE FROM : 1300 APPROX WRAP @ 2000
LOCATION 1 : Stackpole Estate car park. **LOCATION 2 : Stackpole road down to bridge.** **LOCATION 3 : Stackpole centre of bridge.** **LOCATION 4 : Stackpole warren.** **LOCATION 5 : Stackpole red mud path.**	**UNIT BASE: Manor House, The Old Home Farm, Stackpole, Pembroke SA71 5DQ**
WEATHER : Sunny High 16 Low 9 Vis: Good Wind NEN 9mph	**Sunrise: 0654 Sunset: 1926**

UNIT NOTES:

1: BE AWARE THAT WE ARE FILMING NEXT TO LIVE ELECTRICAL FENCES.
2: PLEASE NOTE THE TRANSPORT LIST OF PICK UPS FOR CAST AND CREW AT THE END OF THE CALLSHEET. CALL THE PRODUCTION OFFICE IF THERE ARE ANY ISSUES WITH THE SCHEDULED PICK UPS.
3: BE AWARE THAT WE ARE FILMING ON A LOCATION DESIGNATED AS A SITE OF SPECIAL SCIENTIFIC INTEREST. PLEASE DO EVERYTHING WITHIN YOUR POWER TO MINIMISE IMPACT ON THE LOCAL ENVIRONMENT.

SC	SET / DESCRIPTION	D/N	PG'S	CAST	LOC
24	EXT. NATIONAL PARKS CAR PARK The Boys unpack, James wants to walk	D2	4/8	1, 2, 3, 4	1
	TECHNICAL MOVE				
24A	EXT. OLD LANE They walk down the hill merrily.	D2	1/8	1, 2, 3, 4	2
24B	EXT. THREE ARCH BRIDGE Davy is worried how they will cope with James.	D2	7/8	1, 2, 3, 4	3
27	EXT. CLIFF TOP – PATHS Bill walks past an elderly couple naked.	D2	3/8	1, 2, 3, 4	4
26	EXT. CLIFF TOP – RED PATH James wants to try the go-cart out.	D2	1 3/8	1, 2, 3, 4	5
25 Stunt	EXT. RED MUD ROAD FARMLAND Bill flies through the air. James has only six months left.	D2	1 1/8	1, 2, 3, 4	4
	TOTAL PAGES 4 4/8				

#	ARTISTE	CHARACTER	P/UP	ARR	B'FST	M/UP	COST	READY	ON SET
1	**Benedict Cumberbatch**	**James**	**0540**	**0605**	**0720**	**0620 J**	**0610/0740**	**0750**	**0800**
2	**J J Feild**	**Miles**	**O/T 0600**	**0625**	**0715**	**0650 S**	**0630**	**0750**	**0800**
3	**Tom Burke**	**Davy**	**0600**	**0625**	**0725**	**0710 S**	**0650**	**0750**	**0800**
4	**Adam Robertson**	**Bill**	**0600**	**0625**	**0700**	**0730 S**	**0710**	**0750**	**0800**

S/As C/O Penny Hilling & Cath Morgan	NO.	CALL	COST	M/UP	B'FST	ON SET
Family Sc 24	**3**	**0715**	**As req**	**As req**	**0715**	**0800**
Hiking Couple Sc 27	**2**	**1200**	**As req**	**As req**	**N/A**	**As req**

Total Crowd:5

Production Blog written by Vaughan

September 17th 2009

"LUNDY : South westerly – calm. Fair to good and falling. Squalls later."
My alarm goes at 4am.
I haven't slept much... but then I haven't slept much in days.

I get my work boots on and get in the Land Rover. As I drive to the unit base on the National Trust's Stackpole Estate, I am kept awake by a desire to avoid smearing the myriad of wildlife that use the road as their own at this time in the morning. (I have no grievance against them and I have to drive the actors in this car later. I fear the cull-splatter may disturb the thespianic preparation.) I am listening to the shipping forecast on the radio. For the first time ever I have a really good reason to want to know how the weather on this particular area of our waters – the patch of the Atlantic off the Pembrokeshire coast known to seafarers as Lundy – will affect my day.

For the first time I am about to have my own crew making 'a real movie'. It's exciting. But I can't help but also think about all the millions of things that could easily go wrong between now and the end of the shoot in five weeks time if we get there at all.

The schedule and budget are tighter than my amazing set photographer's skinny jeans.... I wonder, if we do derail, what it will be that finally ends the ride.

I haven't even started yet and I know already that at least two key members of the crew are camped on the borders of insanity – primed to invade that land of lunacy if there is the slightest increase in pressure... and pressure is the one thing I have in abundance for both...

But then as I pull up at the old farm Manor House I see the giant Kitchen truck. We are a small film compared to Nottingham and Harry Potter that have both filmed in Pembrokeshire this summer and yet somehow we've managed to afford a catering truck that may have room for Knight Rider in the back, as well as the kitchen. It glows and steams in the dawn light and excitement swells like a wave inside me. I smell the bacon and the coffee that will fuel the nearly fifty crew.

I greet the location manager who arrives seconds later, and then my partner in production, Kelly Broad who looks like she's arrived for London Fashion week. As the rest of them rock up I greet them with overly gung-ho slaps of encouragement. Knowing that I haven't even closed the finance on the film that I am now DEFINITELY shooting, I wonder if one of the crazy people is me. In fact maybe no one would try what we are about to do if they aren't a few rashers short of a fry up. Its sobering...

But – here's the thing... This is the last moment I have time to consider it.

Before I know it the four actors, Benedict Cumberbatch, JJ Feild, Tom Burke and Adam Robertson are in costume and we're heading to the first shot... The boys are loading the cart that will carry Benedict's character, James, on his journey to Barafundle Bay... and already I'm putting out fires... Telling the designers to find more kit to weigh down the cart (it's a problem because we need it all duplicated for the second unit version of the cart that will be filmed with doubles). I'm also cutting lines from the script, still trying to shrink the scenes... And we're choosing the tree Bill will carry and we're wondering if we actually have permission to use the local cows as background artists... and onwards...

And in the blink of an eye... with some disasters narrowly averted we're on the last shot of the day. Literally as quick as that! With the sun setting behind the headland to the west I tell a white lie to the director about a by-law (I just invented) that prevents Adam Robertson from strolling naked as the script dictates, in the area we had chosen for the shot initially (which is now too far away). We swing the camera round and shoot in a hurry and with failing light that does wonders to shield his manhood, Adam strides naked across the hillside in front of two extras... (played by an old teacher of mine from the school I had attended just down the road)... And suddenly we wrap Day 1.

And we're ferrying the crew back to unit base for a cold beer and to give them the call sheet for day 2. Matt Hanson, the 1st AD, slaps me on the back. I'm exhausted... We all are, but I can't show it. It was amazing and hilarious and fun and terrifying...

The boys did the magic trick that only great actors know how to do. They have conveyed the freedom of the trip they're on – alongside the love and antagonisms of real friendship in just a few moments of film passing behind a lens. We have one day in the can and they look like they've been pushing Benedict in that fucking cart forever already.

I check the last shoot site for rubbish (we will leave everywhere we go on this breath-taking landscape untouched) and head back to unit base...

Along the farm track I pass a farm worker bringing the cows in. I stop to wait for them to pass and he nods and says "Well, you had a nice day for it, boy!"

I nod and drive on and remember how my day started "Calm. Fair to good and falling. Squalls later....". And I realise I don't have enough time to sleep before tomorrow.

September 18th 2009

"DAVY: If the cart breaks..."
On a cliff top. (The novelty has yet to wear off – but then the sun is still shining.)
The First AD and I are worried by the pace we are shooting. I'd like to be cracking the whip here, but even though there isn't much dialogue in this scene I am very aware that this little moment could be one of the most important in the film.

We are running both cameras to catch it. One fixed and one being hand-held in the back of my Land Rover. The camera team squash in there too..... If they scratch my car I'll be livid. Adam who plays Bill (and has been one of my best friends for years) has suggested taping a DV cam to the Cart too. (This is one of his good ideas.)

The shot is still being prepared... The coast path here looks perfect. It strikes us that it looks too perfect! In fact it looks like the fucking 6th fairway at St Andrews! The grass is smooth and even and green. Uniformly trimmed by the fierce hand of mother-nature into this perfect lawn that stretches a hundred miles. I hope we have enough wilderness shots ahead of us to give the film texture.

I think there's something funny about our paramedic. Firstly his ambulance is a rusty banger with the word 'Ambulance' stuck on the side. Secondly his med-kit box looks like he sometimes keeps live fishing bait in it and has done for thirty years. Still – he comes from an official data base and seems a nice chap so I pay it no heed...

It's a scene where ALL the boys climb on James' cart and ride it down a hill. It seems a meaningless little stunt, but if it looks like I hoped it would when I sat alone writing the script, it will be an instantly recognisable image of freedom and 'boyhood' and friendship.

We've tested the speed and route for the descent. Benedict must steer the unstable three-wheeled cart with Adam hanging on the back, JJ on one side, and Tom Burke on the other. It's liable to be very bumpy and fast and near the cliff edge.... but the stuntman is happy and therefore so am I. And the minutes tick by and I'm more concerned about time now than ever... (If we drop a scene we may never get it back.) All cameras are ready including Jamie Stoker's stills camera. Matt the 1st calls ACTION.

The cart rolls forwards, the boys jump on... it slowly gathers pace and jolts down the hill along the cliff edge faster and faster...

It looks amazing. Adam roars with delight! They look they're having the time of their lives. They are.

The shot is in the can. And it's good, but there isn't time to enjoy it. We move on...

(Little did I know at that moment that it would become one of the iconic shots of the film and that one of Jamie's snaps would be used by designer Franki Goodwin to create the poster...)

September 19th 2009

"One day, in a week, a month, a year, on that day when God willing, we all return to our homes again, you're going to feel very proud of what you have achieved here in the face of great adversity."

Col. Nicholson from 'The Bridge on the River Kwai' Directed by David Lean, Written by Michael Wilson and Carl Foreman.

The sun is baking. I thought my problem would be keeping the poorly paid crew with me in the rain and mud... so I budgeted for beer at night. I never budgeted for the bottled water and sun screen we would need in West Wales in mid September... (it can't last can it?) But James' lines about going to his "favourite place on earth – to Barafundle Bay" make more sense when it looks like this – and today is our first day shooting on the actual beach.

Some of the crew haven't seen the beach that at the moment gives the film its title and

they are all suitably awe-stuck by its beauty... This joy lasts a few moments only as they soon realise that we have to carry ALL our kit down the steep steps to the sand. It's the only way down there. And we have to carry it up again every day we're here.

I grab some sand bags that are used as weights for the camera legs and lighting stands and even on my first trip down the cliff I realise what a physical task this film is going to be - and how fucking mental it seems to be carrying sandbags onto a beach.

Eventually we get everything down on to the shoreline and start shooting. The scene involves Adam's character trying to comfort James, who has had a rough night. Jo Evans' make-up is great - Benedict looks really, really ill. We roll camera... there is something almost ethereal about Benedict sometimes. And as he lies in Adam's arms near the high water mark, it's obvious that there are going to be some very special moments in this very special cove.

It's just as well... having had the best of the early light we have to move all the gear to the top again for the next scenes in the schedule.

The steps are steeper and longer when you're going up... as I get to the top for the first time I look down and I can see that the crew are all mucking-in, carrying not just their stuff, but whatever needs to be taken from any other department. Benedict, JJ, Tom and Adam are amongst them carrying gear as well. This is the team spirit I always hoped for and it's the only way we will get this film made.

I head down the steps again. Every crew member I pass has a good natured jibe at me. From the fitter members of the crew I get stuff along the lines of "Couldn't you write about a beach with a fucking car park?!" From the rest – this physical challenge is now hitting home. They just about manage to grunt swear words at me. It takes several trips for most of us to get all the kit back to the trucks on the cliff top. I daren't think about how many times we will have to do this... I think of The River Kwai and start whistling.

September 19th 2009 Afternoon

Miles (JJ Feild): "Well, you really showed that tree."

It's another sunny afternoon. Tom, Benedict, JJ and Adam are lying on the grassy cliff top above me for a scene where Adam (as Bill) hurls the tree that he has lovingly carried throughout the trip, over the edge into the sea.

Some 12 feet below where they are acting is a ledge, a small 'golf green' of grass sloping towards the drop. This is where I am standing with Tom Rogers our lovely assistant location Manager (known as T'other because his boss is called Tom as well.) Our job here this afternoon, out of sight of the camera, is to catch the tree before it descends into the rolling Atlantic.

The night before filming (because somehow they had been forgotten) we actually bought four trees that are identical. Any biologist will tell you that this last statement is impossible, but they are similar enough. The problem is that they were expensive and they are already taking a battering in the natural course of filming for three days.

It's important that Adam throws the tree, which he swings like an Olympic hammer thrower, with all the pent up anger of a man who sees the freedoms of his younger life slipping away. So we don't want to be too constrictive in urging him to aim for a safe landing.

It's an emotional scene and as usual we are pushed for time. The first effort lands easily near us. The second seems to be heading out of reach, but drops short on the rocks above us. The next few takes don't get as far as the throw and T'other and I get lulled into a sense of false security.

While I wait patiently for the slight adjustments in performance, new lenses, and film reloads I fiddle with my phone as if doing so will make it find a signal (I know it won't). So I stand there and again I am aware that for the five weeks of filming this – cliff path above the sparkling sea – is my office.

ACTION! There's the emotional rant from Adam and – knowing that every take may be his last chance – he gives this throw some serious welly. Suddenly there is a tree sailing through the air over me and towards the edge. Without really thinking about the consequences of losing the tree versus losing the tree AND me, I run after it. Its plastic covered root-bag hits the glossy grass and it shoots towards the edge. I dive for it and tackle it a couple of feet before it goes over. Only T'other has witnessed this foolishness I think, and I'm rather glad. (Even though I'm comfortable with the "Don't do as I do – do as I say" school of producing.) My daily safety concerns for the crew should also apply to me. BUT only my co-producer Kelly Broad really understands the constraints of our budget as I do, and I realise that, though she may have done it in heels with far more style and grace, she would probably have gone after that tree too.

Grazed but intact I return the tree to the film's designers (the brothers Campling). The tree has been injured and as we set up for another scene I see that Johnny Campling is super gluing fallen leaves on to the tree's wounded twigs. The magic of cinema.

On JJ Feild

In writing these pieces up I realised I wouldn't really give time to the digressions I would like to… I love a good digression, the possibly reasonless meandering of the mind that one is forced to follow in the hope that maybe, just maybe… anyway.

I have wanted to give time to each of the leads in Third Star. A profile piece if you will. I was never on a set before where the work ethic of the crew was so inspired by the dedication of the actors. They can be regarded as mollycoddled talking props. Not so on our set! They never moaned or complained and they never lost concentration nor – and this is crucial – did they ever lose their good humour or willingness to muck in. So I'm going to do the four the boys one by one – starting with JJ Feild.

I first met JJ back way back in time – when Snickers were called Marathons, when we all believed that the appeal of Take That would never last… and when I plied my trade as an actor too.

We waiting outside a room for a job than neither of us got. This was unusual because it certainly seemed to me that he got most of the jobs we were both considered for.

JJ's had an interesting upbringing, (his father is the British mystic and author Reshad Feild), and he went on to a 'normal' acting training at Webber Douglas. He's one of those guys who doesn't seem terribly out of place anywhere or with anyone. He's obviously creative and can turn his hand to any sport. Interestingly he's very political – (though I would always try to avoid these debates as Adam would always get involved and baiting him amuses me too much and I didn't have time.)

He possesses an old-school charm that is incredibly rare amongst the actors of his generation. The mixture of a calm and classic style with the unquenchable hint of rogue. He is in many ways a blond, very British, Clark Gable.

His laugh is raucous and he can't help but clown around. Usually on our set this involved his humping one of the other boy's legs as soon as the opportunity arose. He's committed and incredibly knowledgeable about the way films are actually made, and never gave up fighting for the best shots and the best takes. Even when off camera his back was so badly injured he could hardly stand, he still carried Benedict up those rocky paths to Barafundle Bay again and again.

Of all his earlier roles I think the first that showed me what a really great actor he is was his performance in Pride at The Royal Court opposite Bertie Carvel. As one of the characters he played in Pride (a repressed homosexual) he had to portray burning self loathing with the facade of character who has found life, seemingly, all too easy – though all the while struggling with his true identity. In other words – he mastered the art of playing dark depths with a subtle lightness that the audience gradually became aware would eventually break with a cataclysmic bang. It was gripping for that.

His lightness is of course not easily played. It drives me mad that so often the good-looking lead is ignored when the 'Rain Man' character is awarded gongs for (forgive me for quoting Tropic Thunder) "100 % retard..."

That these roles are more difficult is a fallacy. JJ IS charming and likeable, but of course being so close to versions of oneself and still being thoroughly entertaining and believable is much harder than 'doing a funny voice'.

As Miles JJ was the perfect choice for all the reasons above.

Miles is competitive and successful. He is a man who has the world at his feet and yet is terrified of all his well hidden failings. His fear is quite literally fear itself. He avoids facing the inner truths by being brutally honest externally with those around him. This makes him arrogant most of the time as it requires the apparent self belief of one who doesn't bat an eyelid when hurting anyone's feelings. We should feel he is even capable of savagery when this willingness to confront the truths outside him requires it. He is in short – the one you want beside you in a fight, but don't expect gentle counselling afterward.

JJ understood this instinctively. He could of course carry off the roguishness with aplomb – but I think he found the ability to KEEP being heartless, KEEP being cowardly in the face of James' plight, the hardest challenge. Of course in the end of the film we understand it all. It's remarkably simple. "I'm scared." is all he really has to say... But the bravery of this collapse, for a man who has created himself as the one you can rely on in your darkest, darkest hour – is chilling and beautiful. And all thanks to something all actors say – but few can actually carry off... "Do it in a look."

I am so lucky to have been able to spend time working with him in rehearsal and of course on set. And our friendship will, I hope carry us through many future films. His latest outing as Union Jack in Captain America is likely to give him a greater global film profile, but I will always be thrilled that he took the long walk in Wales with us.

September 20th 2009

"Satan says to a film producer, 'If you give me your eternal soul I'll make sure your next film makes $200 million.' The producer thinks about it and says 'OK – what's the catch?' "

I'm getting used to answering thousands of questions every day. Until today the first has been 'Do you want coffee?' No longer. The runners now know that I will have been on set since dawn. So the answer will be – YES!

We're on the 4th day of the proper shoot and being the guy where the 'buck stops' for so many questions is what I am here for. But – an embarrassing problem is emerging. The crew keeps quoting scene numbers and I don't automatically know what happens in 23, 69a, 42d…

I don't know whether they expect me to know as a producer or just assume I know because I wrote it. But I don't. I don't like numbers that much. I've seen the script move around a bit of course and sometimes, to be honest, I have watched the actors rehearsing a scene and thought 'Wow. I thought we'd cut that bit'.

Anyway. We are on the cliff above Barafundle Bay. The sun is shining beautifully as ever for the boys' arrival at the bay. We aren't allowed to close the beach, but it's REALLY early on a Monday morning and the first coastal path walkers have been asked very politely to divert slightly or wait a short while so we can shoot the beach at its – remotest.

We have thrown caution to the wind and splashed out on a crane for the camera. It's kind of a giant see-saw, to rise the camera smoothly above the boys and capture on film the virgin beach way beneath us.

The crane guy is here for one morning with his wife. I like him a lot. He has a neat goatee, tattoos and the look of a sporty Iron Maiden fan. He has a small, but immaculate A-Team van (always a sign of a great crewman). I naively I ask where the crane is.

As if by magic, much in the way that Mary Poppins unloaded a floor lamp from her carpet bag, a whole crane quickly and efficiently comes from the small van and in no time at all is ready to use.

Could it be that at last, something is going smoothly? Thanks to Dan-the-crane-man and his professional attitude the faffing is quashed and we are ready to shoot the deserted beach…

Then – I am called to the camera. Matt, the 1st AD, is rubbing his brow with exasperation again because, having masterminded the position of all his runners to block every path to the shore, we have now have just two members of the public who are refusing to move. I peer down at two small dots in the middle of the beach.

Apparently this has been going on for the whole set up of the crane and numerous members of the crew have tried to beg and plead and cajole to no avail. I am of course at the end of this line and the couple on the beach are now costing me thousands of pounds every minute.

I run down the steps that skirt the cliff and across the soft sand. I sink to my knees, panting like a Labrador, beside a middle-aged couple in what look like matching jackets. The lady has some watercolour paints and a sketchpad at the ready, and the man has the facial expression of tax inspector with indigestion and haemorrhoids, who has just found out that his favourite Elaine Paige LP is scratched. Suffice to say I dislike him immediately.

Nevertheless I stick out my hand and smile cheesily and before I can speak he barks at me "Go away. You are harassing us!"

"That's funny." I say "You don't look like you're a rude person. When people smile at me and try to introduce themselves I have been brought up to be more polite."

This opening gambit is a gamble, but he begrudgingly shakes my hand. I tell him my name and that I'm in charge and he tells me his – let's say it's Harold Git for the sake of this.

He then complains for five minutes about the abuse he has received from my crew. The Git-hold up has now meant that about a hundred people are now happily watching us from various points. They are all delighted by the manners and sweet natures of my young Runners. That these Runners have all turned this off ONLY when dealing with Mr. And Mrs. Git is really unlikely (yet, I'm already seeing, understandable). Mr. Git then explains that they have driven for an hour for Mrs. Git to paint her view and that's exactly what they are going to do.

I ask if there is anyway way she could paint the view from elsewhere on the beach where they are not in shot.

NO. In fact he gives me a look that suggests I have just asked for something akin to asking Michaelangelo if he could use Artex on the ceiling of the Sistene Chapel instead.

I explain to Mr. Git that I need them to move for a short while, because we don't have the budget to paint them out digitally, and so their stubbornness will jeopardise a whole day's filming.
NO.
I explain to Mr. Git that we are a small independent film and that losing this shot today will mean we can't afford to reshoot; we won't get the crane back; and will never catch up with the schedule.
NO.
I explain to Mr Git that we will donate some money to a charity of his choice if they would move twenty meters up the beach to sit beside a dune, which will hide them for five minutes!

NO.

For a moment I sit staring at Mr. Twat (Or was it Git?, I'm now changing to TWAT). He tells me to go away and stares at the sea. His tawdry wife's MASTERPIECE is in its early stages, but I can already see that moving them will not be a great loss to the art world. I can think of two options only.

One: I go up to the costume truck, put on Miles' costume, tell Matt to roll camera, come back, drag Mr. Twat down to the sea and drown the bastard, possibly saving me time now and even money later on with divers and water tanks etc. This is preferable, but I imagine there is some film industry small print that precludes it.

Two: I had thought of something that was sure to make him move. Something that only a producer would understand I was capable of doing. (Something that only a producer could be proud of). I was about to earn my wings...

Look. I'm so sorry, but as anti-climactic as it is, I just can't write here what it was that I actually said. But, as the sun beat down, with all the crew and members of the public now watching this little scene from so far away... I told the Twats something that made them agree to move for five minutes.

I ran back up the beach, up the endless stone steps off the cliff. The crane drifted the camera up above the boy's heads to show the wonder and splendour and majesty of their final destination. It really is beautiful. And I'm going to hell.

On Tom Burke

I had been a fan of Tom Burke for a while. Having first seen him in the BBC's Dracula I was immediately struck by the fact that he is gifted with that certain something you can't look away from.

He came late to Third Star. That is to say that for nearly three years, whenever we had auditions we had asked his agents to get him in, only to find he was always busy. It is of course a quirk of fate, as in so many areas of making a film, that lead to his finally being available to come and meet us when we were finally well and truly ready to shoot.

His reading of Davy was perfect. What more can be said?

In his first reading I was able to see at last, right there in front of me, exactly why Davy is my favourite character in the script. Davy is no more confused about life than the other four, but his honesty (about everything that makes his life difficult) makes his fear and uncertainty seem to be far greater. In fact – his honesty make his life the most simple. This is subtle stuff to play at times and where the script lets Davy down, Tom's portrayal more than makes up for it.

Tom is a handsome chap of course, but even in the rushes Davy's calm face gained a kind of enigmatic beauty. For all his over cautiousness and moaning – that beauty comes from inside the character of Davy – and it's why we would all want him as one of our best friends. But the brilliance in being able to create that is all Tom.

That talent would be enough for any actor – but I think what I cherish most from working with Tom on Third Star is that he is one of the funniest bastards I have ever known. I actually think his mind follows paths that only the great comic creators take. He is a skilled writer and I'm sure he'll be an equally talented director.

It was actually only after filming Third Star that Tom and I became close friends. Sometime later Tom did 'Design For Living' at the Old Vic. I went to see it three times and EVERY time, I found that I was still totally enthralled at his performance, in a way that one can usually only experience with someone who maintains a certain mystery, because their real persona is unknown to you. And that mystery is the alluring thing that he naturally possesses – and why he is so fascinating to watch as any character and equally exciting to know in real life.

This week, I am going to see his parents in a play together. His father, well known for his elaborate practical jokes backstage, is David Burke and his mother is Anna Calder Marshall. I'm sure I'm going to see evidence of where 'the talented actor Tom Burke' comes from. But I also know that at some point in the evening, when the lights come up, Tom will say something to me that I could never have expected in a million years. And apart from his love of the work and the text, in writing this, I wonder if it simply his devilish taste for seeing the absurdities of every human around him that drives his talent.

I cannot, for one second, imagine being bored by Tom Burke. And that is about the nicest thing I can say about anyone.

September 24th 2009

Davy (Tom Burke) "That could have been bad."

Today the crew are assembled to film a tricky leg of the boys' journey. In the story, having found the going a bit slow, they decide to cut out what may be a day's walking at their current pace, by lowering themselves and the fully laden cart, down the cliff face on ropes. So we are in the quarry near Barafundle Bay, which has a vertical cliff face that's used for teaching rock climbing, and a mains power source in a hut that also has plumbing.

The Face-pullers – JJ, Benedict, Adam and Tom – are milling around in costume in a clearing at the top of the cliff. There's a qualified team of rock climbers playing with bits of rope that will lower them down. I don't know exactly what they're doing with the rope but they're experts and they seem cheerful. There's our jolly paramedic standing by for this, our biggest 'stunt', with his seventh cuppa of the morning, served from the giant kitchen truck, which is within feet of us for the first time in two weeks. And the rest of the trucks are here too and parked on concrete not sand or cow shit. And there's a real loo! It flushes and everything!

And so – sure – the rope-fiddling seems to be taking a tiny bit longer than normal – but today is already shaping up to be a good day.

No cows. No sea birds. No tide coming in. No boats moored in frame. No walkers sitting in shot painting infantile keepsakes, before going home, having pissed me off on purpose, to eat boil-in-the-bag-cod in front of Songs of Praise! Anyway. You get the picture – TODAY – is a GOOD day.

I go about my business, making sure we are ready for various other things that are coming up. I have a chat with our new Key Grip, the theatrically named, Warwick Drucker, about laying track (that man can LAY –TRACK – by the way. Neat van too. Brilliant. I make a mental note).

Oh – did I mention the sun is still shining?

So then I go up to the top of the cliff for a gentle investigation into the time. The Face-pullers are still relaxed. And there is some amusement amongst the Rope-pullers. One of them wants to tell me something. He's a local guy, part-time fireman. Typically handy looking. He has concerns about the paramedic.

"The paramedic?" I say.

"Yes."

"But he's great, he's been really helpful… and he loaned us a quad bike."

"Well he's not a paramedic."

"Don't be ridiculous. He treated one of the crew a few days ago when his hand was sliced open!"

"Well he's not a paramedic."

"But… he's got a uniform and an ambulance!"

"Well he's not a paramedic."

I look down at that the tubby and affable 'Paramedic'. The rose tinted view fades and I see that his uniform is a tatty green fleece with a badge sewn on. His ambulance is an old Vauxhall Carlton with the word 'Ambulance' stuck on the side, and the whole thing looks like

it's been carrying fish bait for a bit too long. It turns out that this is because it's been carrying fish bait for a bit too long.

I turn back to the fireman-Rope-puller. "....But...But he... What?"

The fireman tells me that the 'Paramedic' is well known to the local emergency crews. He allegedly has his own radio scanner and listens-in to emergency calls. He then likes to turn up first to accidents, especially those involving pregnant women, to lend a hand... He also runs a sex shop on the side... Apparently the BBC made a documentary about him.

"Sorry. Could you say all of that again?"

The colour drains from my face. Behind the fireman-Rope-puller his colleagues are tying Benedict Cumberbatch to a rope that looks thinner than ever and they are about to dangle him of a cliff edge that is suddenly higher and steeper. I tell them to hold on a moment and go for a chat with the 'Paramedic'.

I ask him if he is qualified as a Paramedic. He tells me he is not, but he IS qualified as a Special Emergency First Aid Assistant or some balls.... I ask if he is insured. He says he is. I ask if he can prove that. Now. He says the paperwork would take some time to find... I ask if he has ANY kind of credential on him. He takes out his wallet. It looks like it has been used to shovel the fishing bait into the 'ambulance'. Inside it he finds a business card of considerable age and usage. It has the name of a private medical training company and a phone number so old that its London dialling code places it at least two decades back into history. He asks if someone has said something... I don't answer.

I take it away and race to the office. We phone the number – it doesn't exist. We look into how we found him. He had added himself to the Welsh Screen Commission database. We took this as a credential enough it seems. We were wrong. I ask Kelly Broad to find a new medic because the current one is going to need medical assistance himself in about five minutes.

I go back to set. He is still there though a little sheepish now.

"If this is a company that provides medical training that you paid for I should be able to call them."

He thinks about this rather too long and says. "See, they aren't so much a company, but an... organisation I started in order to -" GET OFF MY SET. NOW.

I am shaking with rage. He drives away quietly. I get a bit shaky. I realise rage has been joined by fear. Fear of what happened there, because of what nearly happened – because of what could so easily have happened. At the office the amazing Ms. Broad has been on the phone.

35 minutes later Adam Robertson is tied to Benedict. They are half way down the cliff because the new paramedic has arrived. He is tall and clean shaven. He is quiet. He has a big shiny Ambulance and a fluorescent uniform. He has an oxygen tank and foil blankets. He has the benign expression of a man who has just washed his hands and can resuscitate a dying woman without getting an erection. He has more qualifications to be there watching no one get hurt than I will ever have for running the whole shebang.

But he doesn't have a quad bike he can lend us. But hey – the sun is shining on the Face-Pullers, Rope-Pullers and on Warwick's track. The smells of cooking from the kitchen fill the quarry and maybe... just maybe we'll catch up the hour we lost. Maybe.

On Benedict Cumberbatch

There is definitely something alien about Benedict Cumberbatch. This was exaggerated the first time we properly met. He arrived late - he often is - but with the flurry of apology that he means utterly, and sounds faintly bored of having to give so frequently. He was wearing his crash helmet and wet weather biker's jacket. It was a modern style so had the moulded Kevlar pads and bumps that shaped his body like an exoskeleton.

He is immediately intelligent. He's on his front foot and yet asking questions. One instantly gets the impression there is no depth to any conversation he is not willing to plumb.

Over the long casting period we discussed with him many times, which of our four leads he could play. What makes him different from most of the actors we saw was of course that he can play so many different parts. Again it's the hint of 'shape-shifter' that gilds his gifts.

At first I was loathe for him to play James (thinking he may play another role). I felt that having become well known for playing Stephen Hawking so brilliantly he would be perceived as some sort of a "rent-a-cripple"... But there was something I needed in James that so few people could portray. And of course Benedict understood it immediately, which is why he is one of the great actors of his generation.

James is a hero. We have to love him. We have to understand why the boys love him and will go to the extreme they do with him... But he's also a bit of a pompous dick. I like to think this is what makes him believable. All these characters have flaws because we ALL do.

But it takes confidence and belief, total artistic commitment and an amazing lack of vanity for a young actor in his first real leading role to know that he can play this character on the edge of likability and get away with it. Of course Benedict does.

The ability to play these complications is another matter. He is of course just a brilliant actor. All the boys were. For me his most impressive ability, as I have said before, is to be technically brilliant, while all the while looking as though there is nothing but gut reaction going on. Watching him physically train to play James (he dieted, ran the cliffs and swam in the cold sea), and also delve into the meaning of every line in rehearsals, and then plot the effect of his illness on his body and mind as it would be in each scene (shot in the wrong order), while all the while being a joy to be around was impressive to witness. To see it as one performance in the final cut was remarkable.

He is rare even amongst the acting breed. If the character description says handsome: he is. If it says Nasty: he is. Older: he is... Younger: he is. For this reason I just can't wait to see what he will become.

Working with him was a delight. I learned so much. It was so often easy to see what he was like at ten years old. He's a giggler, and a brilliant mimic and, like the other boys, he thought nothing of carrying kit up the steps from Barafundle Bay, even after having been on camera all day.

When we cast him in Third Star, his role in Sherlock was yet to make him the global star he is now. This of course did so well for us in one respect and yet his schedule, by the time we released, made it impossible for him to do enough press. Fame had swept him up. And yet, when we talk, I am really aware that he is enjoying it by revelling in the experience of the work far, far more than any of the perks of it.

One evening long after the shoot he called me to ask if he could come to my home to watch Have I Got News For You. "Sure. Why?"

"Because I'm hosting it?"

I sat and watched him watching himself. He was thrilled that he "got away with it", that his suit looked nice; that his memory of people laughing at the right times, on and off script, were real. He was edgy throughout and so relieved when it was over. It was strange to see him so affected by it at first– but of course I realised he was having to be himself. Like the great chameleons of the stage and screen, having to decide on a version of himself to go on camera was a risky business for him.

I'm not sure to what extent that was a turning point, but throughout that period I really felt he had to adjust to life as Benedict Cumberbatch in some way – and he found his feet. Whatever personal doubts he had had, that were inaccurate, are far fewer now. Being really appreciated for what he does best has made him happier in his own skin... So he can spend the rest of his life enjoying wearing other peoples.

Wednesday September 30th 2009

"These are for thinking – these are for dancing." Harry Sivell, most days...

We've moved from the coast to a farm/hotel, Giltar Grove, which is owned by old family friends. (I say that we've moved from the coast– we are in fact about 500 meters from the cliffs even now, but for a change not actually ON a cliff).

The Josephs have been custodians of Giltar Grove all my life. Old Joe Joseph had been a friend of my Dad. I think of my Dad, who died a few years ago, so often of course, but something about being back in Wales and specifically about being my own boss for the first time has made him all the more present in my mind. He was in PR, but would have made a good producer. A confident smile and an acute sense of the ridiculous are key skills for producing.

I used to come to Giltar Grove with him when Joe was alive too. We'd fill sacks of manure with Dad and then stay for drinks and cake in the house. And now, in my many hours of

need on this film, Joe's daughter, Sarah Diment and her husband have turned their home and grounds over to THIRD STAR and adopted me (and the loud and messy crew of 50 who follow me about at the moment.) The extended Joseph clan all live on the farm in various houses or in other farms in the hills around us. It's special. They are special. And every time Sarah mentions my Dad I can't help but think he'd be overjoyed that I was here with my circus and them.

The house is doubling as the home of James (Benedict Cumberbatch) and today we are shooting the opening scenes of the film where James is enjoying a birthday, his last, and the arrival of his companions for the coming adventure. The designers have a lot to do to make the party look real… come to think of it… where ARE the designers?

As Benedict relaxes in the sunshine, in his 40's suit and wide brimmed hat, ready for the first shot, news reaches me that the set designers are sick and can't work.

Most days this wouldn't be too bad. They make sure we have the right cart and kit, and they make sure the campfires are lit and sustained, but the coastline does the rest… It's not too 'design heavy'. Today however is one of the two BIG set ups. Today they have to design a party and all its trappings. They have to bring a family home to life.

It's not normal for crew to go sick. It's not really possible. Everything is too specialised, too dependent on each crew-member being the cog of the rolling wheel that CANNOT stop. So crews are used to being hardy and carrying on. And the designers – the Campling brothers – are tough as old boots and so this is particularly unlucky.

Mild panic sets in. We are working too slowly as it is. I'm at a loss as to know how to fix this and now we have no set! I know we cannot stop, or slow down any more than we have… As ever Kelly Broad (co-producer in this venture) laughs with me and then sets off to do what she needs to do. She rallies the runners to become the designers. Richard Campling appears from his deathbed to give some pointers and relevant info. I've never seen a man look so ill who wasn't actually in the wing of a hospital where normal people shouldn't go. To make things worse for him all the info' he needs to impart is about what 'party food' they have bought already or suggestions for what we should get. He visibly heaves with every mention of cocktail sausages.

We're going to waste time, but there's nothing else to do... And then, as Kelly sets about transforming the dining room I hear there is another problem.

James's sister is played by the beautiful Nia Roberts, dressed by Welsh designers TOAST, and she is standing by, but her boring husband – from whose arms she has strayed in to the embrace of Miles (JJ Feild) is a no-show. It's not a big role of course, but his appearance as part of the 'normal' happy family life is vital.

We cast our eye around the male members of the crew or any passing male from the Joseph clan... He's got to be a bland, generic, banker type... All agree it should be me.

(I'd like to think this is based on my previous acting experience...)

So – a runner is dispatched to pick up new clothes for me. I run from beside the camera to the makeup department where I shave the producer's stubble. My hair is given a side parting and I put on some glasses. With the help of the "smart casual" look I am suddenly "Mike... Banker". It's horrible.

Eventually the party has been thrown together and I find myself, after a long time away from it, ON CAMERA again.

The scene involves Bill being bored to tears by Mike at the party, with Davy looking on sympathetically. Then Miles arrives...

So we end up doing loooonnggg takes, WITH SOUND, where I am having to ad-lib to Bill (Adam Robertson) about nothing in particular but in character. Being as boring as possible, with only the odd prompt from him if I run out of steam. (While I do this I am aware that the party set design delay has eaten more time than Tom Burke has eaten prop food).

Now - it's also relevant to say here that Adam has been one of my best friends since we met as young actors, fresh from drama school. He was my first business partner in Western Edge Pictures and therefore we know each other pretty well.

Take One: I set off rambling about buying wine online. As we make eye contact I see the slightest tweak of a face muscle that denotes Adam's attempts not to corpse – and I'm gone. We both break into raucous laughter and the camera has to be reset. (Time and film wasted by me.)

Take Two:... I ramble about wine buying and the internet and again Adam is grimacing, looking away from me as he tries not to laugh and again I crack.... and so on...

Take SIX: I feel the giggles coming first and take a sip of juice to try and control it. It works. But this gives Adam the chance to speak. (Adam is a huge talent but ad-libbing, I'm sure he'll agree is not his strong point.) "And you also collect... shoes?"

I collapse. This time we're laughing so hard we can't remain on the chairs and Tom Burke is helpless also. No-one is saying anything or complaining. I am of course 'the boss', (in fact there is apparently a crowd around the monitor) but I am all too aware that if this were not me I'd be getting fucking impatient and trying to get this moving faster.

As the takes roll by the agony increases...

TAKE TEN: Now I can't look at Adam at all. I am focusing on a point on the table and just trying to speak as dully as possible, trying to actually listen to myself, but without fail I either hear Adam snort, or catch Tom's face out of the corner of my eye and I'm gone again. It's humiliating to be exposed as having a total lack of control!

By the afternoon we have moved to the scenes after the party and 'boring Mike' is blessedly consigned to history. I am back in work gear and myself again – and trying to get us shooting faster. There's an Exec from our finance partners (Nigel Thomas from Matador) on set for a visit and he can see the problems we're having getting this film shot on schedule. I'm so glad he wasn't there for my 'performance'.

In the evening I have dinner with him in the beautiful, ancient Plantagenet Restaurant in Tenby. Nigel is good fun, but tough. He's a veteran of many films and talks me through my options. I have tried them all already. "Ah well, he says…", calm and benign as ever. "You'll finish the film on time."

"Will I?"

He smiles knowingly, remembering perhaps what it was like to be in my shoes once and glad that he is no longer there…"Yes." He says. " You just… will."

I'll be on set by 5 a.m. again, solving problems, but we order another drink. I realise there is a producer's club, and I'm in it.

I think of my Dad again… He'd often tap his head and point to his feet and say "These are for thinking these are for dancing."…

On Adam Robertson

Adam and I met while playing teenage school boys in a 'Taggart' feature – his first job out of drama school. I was the good guy, he was the bad guy… our roles in real life soon reversed. Adam is a moral compass. (You just have to know how to hit it when it gets stuck.)

After years of friendship, during which we had both made the mistakes in life that most of the people I find I like best seem to have similarly made, we went for a long walk. On our walk I told him I had been thinking that he should join me in a new kind of film and theatre company. By that time Adam was about to start running a vegetarian food business out of Borough Market with his lovely new wife Anna, but acting and producing had always called him away from the various other businesses and sensible jobs he had done so successfully.

A week later he'd read all the stuff I'd written so far and agreed that he wanted 'in' on the company, which we then named Western Edge Pictures. We sat on the South Bank and decided pretty quickly that we wouldn't make a 'short', as so many industry insiders in the UK feel is necessary. We wanted to go straight to a feature.

"Any ideas?" he asked, as we watched the grey Thames oozing towards the sea in front of The National Theatre.

"Well, I have this idea about some boys on a camping trip in west Wales..."

One of the first things I did in writing the story was cast Adam in my head, as Bill.

Adam is a good man. He cares about people and the world equally. His goodness is infectious to most people, and hilarious to me. His goodness has a bluntness. A straight, heavy, indelicate absurdity that no matter how sincerely expressed – I just can't take it seriously. (Of course my seat in Hell is already paid for, but recognising the humour in his finest quality is at least what makes the character of Bill so watchable in Third Star I think.) You can totally see in Adam's role, even though their views are poles apart, exactly why the other boys – indeed why we ALL – would love to have a Bill in our lives – and why I need Adam Robertson in my own.

So, skip forward to pre-production. It becomes obvious that Third Star is going to be a bit 'bigger' than we first imagined and the producing is going to need both of us full time. Adam immediately stepped aside from acting. He didn't NEED to be a movie star. The film was more important. But a strange thing happened. The more we auditioned guys, with Adam reading Bill for guys trying out to be James, Davy and Miles, the more obvious it became that no one – no matter how good – was going to replace him as Bill. It seems crazy now to imagine we wouldn't have cast him. (It also seems crazy to imagine that we would have made the film without Kelly Broad who we brought in at this point to replace Adam in production. Another lasting friendship and partnership was created there – but that's for another day.)

Over the coming months the cast was solidified around Adam. And he was unwittingly still providing me with dialogue for the film. "Biscuits... they're great on their own – but dip them in tea – it's a whole other journey." A direct quote from Adam in the office that he would repeat as Bill on camera a year later.

That's not to say there is no divergence between the character and the man. The complications of real life are after all inevitably greater than those of any invention. Adam is also considerably brighter than Bill (no matter how well he hides it).

He is sensitive and passionate and for all his confidence and bombastic Alsatian pup-exuberance, arriving on set threw him a little. After all our hard work on bringing our first Western Edge picture to production, exactly as we planned to, I noticed a rare uneasiness about him in the first few days. Eventually I was able to ask him how he was doing and he admitted to being a little in awe of what we had achieved, and a little humbled by the opportunity to shoot in that location, with such a great crew, and with such a heavyweight cast. I was amazed. No one could deserve it more. No one could understand how we had got there more clearly than he and I – but where I, thrilled though I was by all of it, had begun already to be frustrated by the small scale, his humility was touching. Where so many men about to star in a film would find their ego taking over – he experienced a fleeting moment of doubt in his otherwise sure-footed stride though life.

Within days of course he was well into the groove. He went up a gear in fact. There are still so many 'Bill moments' that make me laugh. And his delivery of the line "Why can't you take an overdose like normal people?" that he so effortlessly imbues with the innate humour and the gut wrenching tragedy simultaneously, as only great actors can, is just one example of his huge talent.

Any actor will tell you that playing close to yourself is the hardest gig you'll get. Adam had to get his version of Bill spot on and all the while receiving less care than I gave to the other cast. He triumphed.

We opened the film in his native Scotland, at the Edinburgh Festival. Adam had won one of the festival's Trailblazer awards for exciting newcomers and was determined to enjoy the experience "to the max". I realised, in a rare moment of warmth, that seeing that big-hearted freak on the red carpet in his kilt was pretty much all the reward I needed for the journey he and I had shared. His joy was typically unfettered, uninhibited and honest. Somewhere between an overgrown Hobbit on his way to a rave, and a young Sean Connery – as if shouldering the mantle of being the next King of Scotland would be as easy as breathing.... Long live Adam Robertson.

October 3rd 2009

"It's not your fault. It's just really, really, really, really, really, really, really unlucky" The Beachcomber

Hugh Bonneville is here to help us do the impossible.

In the film James, Miles, Davy and Bill stop for coffee at a cove littered with flotsam and jetsam. Amongst it they are surprised to meet 'The Beachcomber'. This eccentric man is one of the characters that make the trip something of an odyssey. He tells the boys a strange story about how he spends his days looking for a lost consignment of faulty, brown Darth Vader action figures. They were swept off a container ship nearby some years earlier and he believes this cove will eventually be the place that they are all washed ashore by the rolling tides. It's a nod towards the part in so many of us that are searching for something that we may never find.

It's been a favourite part of the story for most people who have been involved in the development. I love that The Beachcomber gets interpreted in so many different ways. It is meant to throw up questions about what makes life worthwhile. And it's lovely that the Beachcomber instinctively sees the gentle kindness of Davy, having spent too many years alone with his thoughts, suddenly remembering the value of community, and friendship; in needing people, and in being needed… But OH MY GOD… this little episode is running at well over ten pages and we only have a day with Hugh to shoot it. I brace myself for a day of fighting to get things shooting faster than ever. (The bit of my job that I hate.)

It's 6am. I've been running around a while already trying to sort out the day's fresh load of compromise when I'm told that Hugh has asked to talk to me. Immediately I think something must have gone wrong. I know his hotel is nice and we haven't forgotten his breakfast - he can't have been here long enough for us to fail him in any other way surely? I look around the morning mayhem – maybe he has. I knock on the door of the green room where he is changing and preparing.

I'm thrilled that he has taken time out to come do this role. I have been a fan of Hugh for so long. He seems the most 'natural' sort of actor on stage and screen with a gift for gravitas and exquisite comic timing – and here he is – staring seriously at the pages of the script. He looks up with an equally stern expression and I am ready for the complaint, in fact I almost apologise involuntarily. Of course the complaint never comes. He breaks into a broad smile, assures me that he is comfortable, happy to be here and looking forward to hanging out with Benedict, JJ, Tom and Adam. Then his stern expression flicks on again and he tells me he wants to talk about the script.

"Oh!" I exclaim. Rather taken aback. I have sort of forgotten that's my job as well.

I sit down opposite him as he launches in to a detailed question about the meaning of one of his early speeches. Only now do I notice that he is wearing alarmingly small, denim hotpants.

Thankfully the shock subsides when I realise these are half of his ludicrous costume. But I don't have the time or inclination to over-examine this as Hugh rattles through the ten pages asking if he can move the odd line. Cut a bit here. Add a bit there… He even says that he remembers a line from an EARLIER DRAFT that had a phrase he thinks was important. He's so right. It IS important. I tell him that he should put it back if he'd like to. A few minutes later, he's done and I leave him pawing over the words. I walk down the stairs with a spring in my step. It lasted five minutes, but it was an insight into the incredible talent, skill and knowledge of a REAL PRO. A no-nonsense, business-like, approach to the job of bringing the Beachcomber to life the very best way he knows how. I am so proud to have been the writer (and producer) that will benefit from it and it is again proof that actors are horribly underused in the development of films.

I am determined that any film that Western Edge Pictures makes will have this input from as early as possible and that the writer is always in the room to hear it. And we'll make damn sure that this all happens long before the actor in question is wearing his denim hotpants.

I tell a runner to "take more tea to Mr. Bonneville straight away!" – she looks at me confused as it's only been a few minutes since she did exactly that – I just want to give him SOMETHING – and it's all we have. "And make it hot… or strong or something!"

A while later. We are on the rocky cove. Hugh looks hilarious but the women on set seem suitably pleased to gaze at him. His performance is breathtakingly good. He makes catchphrases of some of the smallest lines – wistfully opening the door to the pain and confusion in the soul of this lost man with just the subtlest of gestures and intonation. It's a masterclass.

But as ever I'm worried about the time. We cannot waste a second today. And Hugh is getting progressively colder and more uncomfortable as a light rain starts to fall and dampen his hotpants. Then something rather wonderful occurs to me. Today nature is on my side and in a way that couldn't be more apt, she is on the side of our Beachcomber. We CAN'T run over time and it isn't ME that has to hurry the proceedings at all today – because the tide is coming in.

I notice that the sea is now lapping at the feet of Moritz, our young lighting apprentice, who is holding a reflector at the edge of our 'set'. He is Bavarian and made of too stout a stuff to even acknowledge it, but nevertheless the Atlantic has decided we should move on and it won't take no for an answer. I sit back and watch Hugh. He must be tired, but doesn't complain.

'Time and tide wait for no man' and at last we are done. Hugh is taken to meet a train. I won't get to see quite how good his scene is for some weeks yet. His day on set seems like it's been at least two.

At this point I'm told that we don't have a night security guard and someone has to stay there all night to watch the vehicles, make sure the pig is roasting properly for the next day's carnival scene, then turn on the kitchen truck at 3 am to power the freezers and heat everything in time for the crew's breakfast. I sigh.

The last of the crew leave. I sit alone with a beer in one hand and my 'Night Security Torch' in the other. I sit on the bonnet of the Land Rover looking at the cove. The pig is rotating slowly on the spit – looking at me every 37 seconds as if to say "You think you've got problems!", the seagulls are settling on the cliffs and the tide is starting its endless turn again.

Monday October 5th 2009

"If I said you had a beautiful body would you hold it against me?" The Bellamy Brothers. And the ferry man from "Barafundle Bay."

We've moved further up the coast to a deep rocky cove called Martin's Haven, where real little ferry boats cross to some of the islands off the Pembrokeshire coast, where people go bird-watching.

We are shooting the scenes of the boys meeting a strange man selling tickets for the ferry and the scenes on the ferry itself where James (Benedict Cumberbatch) will have a heart to heart with the skipper.

In reality one doesn't need to cross a ferry to get to Barafundle Bay, but I wanted the journey to have the hint of being an odyssey and meeting this ticket seller (an archetypal gatekeeper) and then the ferryman (an ancient symbol of crossing over from one life to the next) is part of that goal. I love the idea of these double meanings and symbols throughout. I almost want the boys to look back at each incident and ask themselves if it really happened. By the end of the story the greater questions of whether they should go on or turn back, help James or not, live one way or another are at the heart of the film.

As we build the ticket sellers hut, a shed with a neon sign, plonked on the beach, a young seal rolls around on the shore at our feet as if shamelessly hoping to be cast.

Karl Johnson is the ticket seller. He steps into his shed dressed as a gruff old sea dog, but wearing full eye make-up and suddenly looks as though he's been there for years.

His scene goes well. He and Tom Burke have known each other a long time and off camera they stay in character being funnier than I could ever write them.

When the scene is done we say a reluctant goodbye to Karl and the boys head on to the ferry. On board, while the other boys fool about, James and the Ferryman (played by the lovely Welsh actor Philip Madoc) get into a chat about the journey of life. They share something. Neither have long left.

I want the scene to try and remove some of the sentimentality from the script by saying that searching for the definitive answers to the strange questions that life throws up is utterly pointless. Neither man knows what is coming next, neither believes in a higher power necessarily, but the ferryman has worked out that most of the complications we meet are not worth thinking about for a single moment. Finally James asks him if he has had a good life. The ferryman thinks and says "Yes – But then I never asked much of it."

Thursday October 8th 2009

"The major difference between a thing that might go wrong and a thing that cannot possibly go wrong is that when a thing that cannot possibly go wrong goes wrong it usually turns out to be impossible to get at or repair." Douglas Adams, Mostly Harmless

Despite nearing the end of the shoot it seems I am still the only one who can draw out cash for the film's daily expenses. With alarming regularity the production office tell me to go and withdraw about seven grand... sometimes ten!

This is annoying as it forces me to leave the set for half an hour or so, which I dare not do, or it means I race off during lunch – which means I don't get to check-in with people and our daily problems... and I don't get to eat! (Our caterers are amazing and I love and NEED lunch.)

Today the call for cash was urgent so I raced into the nearest town to get the money. The first time I did this, a few weeks ago I learned that withdrawing seven thousand pounds on a normal Wednesday afternoon from the Barclays Bank in Pembroke is not possible.

The teller laughed and called other staff over to laugh at me as well. I stood there, dusty and tired, missing lunch, holding open a cotton sack and glancing furtively at my watch.

"Seven thousand!? Here?! We don't have that, love!"

"Oh... I assumed, being a bank and all... Uh, how much CAN I have... ?"

At this point it was starting to sound more like a hold up than a legal withdrawal, but with less satisfactory results. After much debate they worked out that if I raided another two branches I would be able to make up the seven grand. They phoned ahead to warn them of my arrival... from another world. Film world. Anyway – we have learned to order cash in advance, but it still annoys me that I have to leave set today to go into the bank.

While on my way there I suddenly come over the brow of a hill and a rare sounds echoes through the Land Rover. My phone is ringing. I have barely had a signal for nearly five weeks so this is an event. But it's not good news.

"Vaughan – you need to come on set. The council have turned up and shut us down."

We are filming at Freshwater West today. A stunning beach where filming for Robin Hood and Harry Potter also occurred. But to be exact – at the moment we are doubling up the location and using the interior of the toilets in the car park (where JJ Feild is meant to have his Rolex stolen by the Angel Boy). Apparently a cleaner arrived. Didn't know anything about us and called his boss, who called his boss, who sent a man in a van with an order to cease and desist or the police would be called. I won't bore you again with the 'time vs money' problems of this shoot but suffice to say THIS. CANNOT. HAPPEN.

I skid to a halt. The crew are sunbathing around the dunes besides the car park above the beach. Benedict is in costume playing Frisbee with some of them. In the centre of the car park is a Pembrokeshire County Council van. A tall man who is "just doing his job" is leaning against it.

My arrival causes some stirring in the crew. Whatever I am about to do I'd rather it didn't have the audience, but it can't be helped.

I walk towards the man, let's call him Steve... I actually think he was called Steve... So let's call him Dave, and as I do I try to work out something, if possible, about him, to help formulate a plan for my approach. I am no Sherlock it seems – and I'm getting closer – so, for some reason, with a tone that suggests I've missed him terribly – I say "Hi there! How are you?"

Though as a desperate producer I am prepared to bend my morals in this encounter I decide the moral high ground is one I'll try first and I begin with the most abject apology for wasting his valuable time. His expression softens, but I realise he is also now considering how valuable his time that morning actually is, and that perhaps, hanging about in this car park is... well... a fairly normal use of it. Nevertheless – that I value it more highly than Pembrokeshire District Council intrigues him if not endears me to him.

I shepherd him to our catering truck and soon a coffee is in his hand. I have made the necessary call to our location manager Tom from the car on the way and Tom assured me the suitable permissions will be in place asap. The problem is that there is no evidence at all of this and this 'Dave' – is not only the guardian of the toilet, but currently holds the completion of the entire film in his hands.

I can't recall exactly what I said, but I know it was in the vein of Ford Prefect in the beginning of The Hitchhiker's Guide' convincing the council Rep' to lie down in front of his own bulldozer so Arthur Dent could take a break from protecting his house.

I basically managed to confuse the timing of the necessary phone call he would get with the message that we can recommence filming, with the act of our actually recommencing the filming. I was verbally back-dating the former with the latter to make the latter possible immediately, as the former was of course 'a foregone conclusion', which therefore made his staying here only a further waste of his time, as we would be already be filming anyway, 'though of course he is welcome to stay and watch! Love to have him there!" – but it would of course mean that he was unable to drive away to get a signal that would definitely mean he could receive the phone message that gave us permission to recommence the filming, which we were already doing...He scratched his head. I made fast circling motions with my hand behind his back – the signal to the crew to recommence filming.

A short while later, as Dave drove away with some cake, our breathless location manager (dear Tom Jenkins) turned up with news that we now had the permission to use the toilet and explained how the error had occurred (not his fault at all for the record.) It didn't matter. We had dropped a few minutes, no more. And the scene was being completed. As the First called lunch I sighed and got back in my car. Co-Producer Kelly stroked my head. "Well done. Where are you going? " "The fucking bank!" "Oh... I'll save you some lunch." As I drove out of the car park again I remembered the words of Douglas Adams, one of my favourite writers; "Time is an illusion. Lunchtime doubly so."

Friday October 9th 2009

"Can't we just light the fuckers here? " Miles

For nearly the whole shoot we have had the four guys together (as the script requires). This has been nice in one way – but early on we became aware of the problems of constantly shooting a 'dinner party' in terms of angles and coverage. On many occasions, with things happening so slowly, I wished the idiot writer had foreseen this and written a few more scenes with just two guys talking...

Today however, we're on Freshwater West and JJ Feild and Benedict Cumberbatch have a moment alone together. So, I go off with Adam Robertson and Tom Burke to film some stuff. Our second camera/B crew have been totally amazing throughout – great characters who created their own infectious team-spirit. As well as being the second camera for the scenes of the four stars, they have also captured so many great shots of the doubles enjoying the miraculously warm weather. (In fact earlier on they nicknamed themselves "28 Sunsets" as they set out in a 4×4 to capture the "magic hour" of every evening in the schedule.)

So we've run both cameras pretty much all day, every day. Our camera department budget, and most alarmingly our film stock budget, has doubled. With my producer-hat on I had to explain this to our financiers, but when they saw just some of those sunsets they seemed happy... No that's a lie. Not happy. They just didn't shut us down. "They seem happy! Let's move on..." is just what I told anyone who asked about it.

Today I get to muck around a bit though, getting some stuff of Burke dropping little pebbles in a rock pool contemplatively – only to have Robertson drop a boulder into it from behind him. In doing his shock response Tom makes the most hilarious roaring noise – once again proving his comic genius.

These scenes are nearer the end than the beginning of the journey and over the next few days we will shoot some of the saddest, as the shoot draws towards a close. But tonight we film a firework display and the comedy of the camp catching fire. It's a long night. The hours I spent in the script wondering how we will manage to shoot this mishap are about to be answered.

We are now well into October. The temperature drops. We huddle in the dunes as the last flocks of birds leave for sunnier climes. Darkness descends and the props guys send a rocket down a wire into the tent, treated with fire retardant to make it burn slow enough to catch on camera. (It still goes up in seconds). Then we shot the actual fireworks. JJ, Tom and Adam are brilliant fools on and off camera and, as he watches the ill-judged display above them (a section of the script I titled "My Firmament Falling Down" in a very early version) the look on Benedict's face pretty much says it all... By midnight it's freezing and as we pack up for the day and hurry to warm cottages, I'm aware that the gracious welcome of this coast may be about to run out.

Thursday October 15th 2009

Brody: What day is this?
Hooper: It's Wednesday... eh, it's Tuesday, I think.
Brody: Think the tide's with us?
Hooper: Keep kicking.
Brody: I used to hate the water...
Hooper: I can't imagine why.

Today is the last day of the shoot in West Wales. (There's one more day's filming, at a special underwater tank in East London). It's an irony fitting of the finale to such an "incident" filled shoot that around mid-morning Kelly Broad comes on set to whisper in my ear that she'd had the call we've been waiting for. We have now finally 'closed the finance'. In other words we can now go ahead and shoot the film. Kelly and I laugh.

Luckily the crew have only needed to concentrate on the job in hand. But while we are all fitter, stronger, very tanned (unbelievably) and have found a great rhythm, I can also see that everyone is tired.

The cast in particular have been amazing, uncomplaining and have led the effort with their talent and resolve. But being together as these four characters in EVERY shot has taken its toll. A couple of nights ago, in a scene where they discuss the after-life while stoned, we all politely waited as Tom Burke gave a particularly long dramatic pause before saying his next line. The camera rolled on and on before JJ finally looked round at him and realised he had fallen asleep in the middle of a take. He awoke at the sound of our laughter and calmly said "Oh. Is it me?"

Last night we shot the last scenes on the beach itself. Benedict crying out in pain was truly disturbing. The chilling sound echoed out into the night across the bay.

Not since I finished writing it have I been really alone. I love being part of a crew. But the day after Wales Wrap it's just Kelly Broad and I left to clean 'the Manor House' at Stackpole – our unit base. I found it nearly four years earlier and now while packing it up the sadness really hits me. We dismantle the phones and pack up our numbered mugs. We empty the costume rooms, the make-up rooms, the Greenroom where the boys ate so many odd breakfasts and empty the fridge in the kitchen where we ended so many long, hot days with cold beers. The rare horseshoe bats that live in the attic will have it to themselves again.

Every so often one of the crew stops by to pick up something or leave something with us before they head back east and to their next job. We thank them for all their hard work and hope I'll have them on a film-set again soon. I hand the keys back to the guys from the National Trust. "Well, you were lucky with the weather anyway…" Yes. Yes. Yes. We were. At last – I take down the banner that hangs over the door. I roll it up and toss in the back of my mud and manure-caked Land Rover. It reads "Welcome to Barafundle Bay".

I pick up Benedict from his cottage and we leave the green and blue of the West behind us. As we drive I start to face the battles ahead – to turn our footage into a film and then get that film released… Fuck. There is so far to go. Then my phone rings.

One of our assistants, back in London already, tells me that Tom Burke was dropped at a train station in Carmarthen and then found that he'd lost his wallet. He has no ticket and therefore no way home. (Over the next two years I will discover on my travels with Tom that this not an unusual event.) Forty-five minutes later I pull off the road and collect him from the roadside. Another companion for my return to the Big Smoke.

"So Tom, we didn't get to talk much during filming. I'm sorry. I was so busy. How was it for you? …Tom? " Benedict looks into the back. "He's asleep…"

"Oh… So what about you, mate? You got anything else lined up?… Hm… Well, let's chat about it. We have plenty of time now…"

Friday October 16th 2009

"We are such stuff, As dreams are made on; and our little life, Is rounded with a sleep."
Prospero, William Shakespeare's The Tempest

This is meant to be the last day of the shoot. The coast of Pembrokeshire is 250 miles west of us and I miss it already. We are at an industrial estate in Essex at a specialised diving tank trying to get the shots of what happens below the surface with Benedict Cumberbatch and JJ Feild. The tank is 7m deep (easily deep enough to drown a face-puller or two). It's also surprisingly warm and VERY chlorinated. The little old guy that runs it is sort of an East End Jacques Cousteau – bobbing about the place helping our underwater Camera team. The first thing we do is try to match the colour of the water in the tank to the colour of the water in the sea off Barafundle Bay.

One cold blustery day, way back before the beginning of the shoot, our chief underwater cameraman came on a recce with us to Barafundle Bay. While I was counting the steps up the cliff with very little glee, he took a stroll with his DVcam. When we watched his footage later it was quite startling. The grey sky and grey surface of the water quite suddenly switched to an almost fluorescent PEA GREEN as the lens dipped under the surface – it was hard to believe. This colour change was extant while filming the boys at sea, right through the shoot.

So here we are, back in the tank, and I'm watching as the divers pour in large cans of food colouring (used in the manufacture of mushy peas and baked beans) in just the right amount, stirring it by swimming with their large flippers, to try and match the colour of the tank to picture on a monitor.

[This turns out to be a TOTAL waste of time. In the edit we discover that making the colours so real just didn't look... well ... REAL. Every time we cut to an underwater shot the difference in colour looked more like it was shot in a tank than the tank actually did in the first place. Luckily we use very little of the underwater footage and end up digitally greying the water to match it closer to the look of the surface. Inaccurate, but better. This is one of those great little lessons in filmmaking that I tuck away in my mind for the future.]

While Benedict and JJ get ready, we watch the assembled rushes of the scenes above the water in the Atlantic to try and match performance too. All our minds went back to those days shooting...

... Sunday 27th September 2009

Today we're going to get in boats, take our four stars out into the bay and film them as they try to give their best friend the ultimate gift they can. His freedom. Today we are going to drown Benedict Cumberbatch.

Usually the days I liked best are those where something else (like a stunt, or special effect) takes the pressure to be the ball-breaker out of my hands. But even though the divers will be in charge of how safe the boys are, and therefore what we can or can't shoot and for how long, I have a knot in my stomach. This is my first film in charge and my stars are about to float around freely in the Atlantic Ocean. It's cold. It's bound to be time consuming. Too much can go wrong... And yet it is perhaps the most important sequence of the film.

So, with wetsuits under their costumes, and wearing flippers to make treading water easier, the boys (Adam Robertson, JJ Field, Benedict Cumberbatch and Tom Burke) head off. They look nervous for the first time.

The dive cameraman has told me that our actors will not be able to last more than fifteen minutes in the ocean before being plucked out to dry off and warm up. This is the Atlantic and we are nearly in October. Then they'll then need at least an hour before they can go in again. We light a fire on the beach and have tents and soup and towels and clothes ready for this process revolving. But he also tells me that as the day goes on the fifteen minutes shooting-time will get shorter and shorter. When he thinks they are too cold he is pulling them out though. No argument.

This is why there is a knot in my stomach. Though there isn't much dialogue, filming on and in water is incredibly difficult. Basically EVERYTHING is moving. All the normal stuff like changing a lens, even moving to another angle, just eats away at the time. Fifteen minutes can vanish in a blink – and suddenly the boys will be too cold and have to come out.

The boats are loaded and gun their engines to get around the headland into the deep water off Barafundle Bay. The sea is whipping up into the faces of the actors. I am wondering if we have bitten off more than we can chew. What if one can't take it and the others can? What if one gets sick? What if we can't get the right shots to tell the story anyway? This is the ending of the film? It's possibly the end of my career. Why didn't I write a film set in a car park? With their usual humour the boys take off their coats. Adam leads them – and jumps into the sea. They follow one by one.

Back in the tank in Essex we are looking at the rushes from that day, roughly assembled into the above surface drowning sequence. The shots really do speak for themselves. We're all remembering that really was a remarkable day. Treading water in that kind of cold, in the currents of sea, while concentrating on what they are trying to do was exhausting. And of course that exhaustion worked so well to convey the truth of what the characters had come through to get there. Even some of the hardened crew found it quite affecting to film.

[With all four boys still alive and kicking – I hope it's ok to reveal that in fact they stayed in

for longer than 15 minutes every time they got in the water. In one shot they stayed in the water for over 40 minutes. They never complained. They just wanted to get it done and get it done right. Though they lost quite a few pairs of flippers that I had to pay for…]

Seeing them drag Benedict back to shore, forming the end tableau, the result of the journey was every bit as striking as I had hoped it would be.

The tank is a different challenge for JJ and Benedict. The temperature of the water being the biggest difference of course. The tank has windows at the bottom so I can watch the boys as they take breaths from the diver's aqualung to stay underwater as Miles (JJ) holds James (Benedict) until he gives up the fight for a life he no longer wants.

By the end of the day the chlorine has taken its toll on them. Their eyes are red and burning. They look like rabbits that have had makeup tested on them. After surviving the Atlantic without a mutter of discontent, they are now whimpering in agony.

With some time left on the clock though, we decide to capture some scenes of the boys swimming on the surface from beneath the water. Except we only have two of them. Luckily, we do have the costumes and the young, rather bemused, diving tank assistant agrees to don Davy's outfit as a swimming double. We just need someone to be Bill.

It is fitting as a final addition to my CV of jobs on this film that it is me. I delight in telling the 'making of' camera that the waist on Adam's trousers is way too roomy for me and I dive in. As I swim across the tank with Benedict and JJ I'm thrilled to be one of them for a moment. They are laughing and endlessly willing, but they really do look pretty fucked.

Finally it's a WRAP. "Barafundle Bay" is in the can.

I will see the lads again of course, when we get in to the sound studio at the latest, with a finished cut of the film. But – there's a whole lot of editing to do first. It's an emotional farewell. I get home at last. I have some beers. I feel empty.

Every film maker I know says that a schedule must include getting ill after a shoot, as the body is allowed to shut down. But, having become a challenge-junkie I decide not to give in to this and go out and play rugby the next day. And break my collar bone.

Only after this does it all hit me. The morning after, I can't get out of bed. I lie there letting the whole film wash over me. Dozing, I let myself drown in it all.

I get up at 2pm. At 2.30pm I realise that I have been upright for 30 minutes without people asking me questions, without the need for decisions – I seem to be in slow motion.

Perhaps it is just to do something, or perhaps it's some weird subconscious metaphysical need to cleanse, but I decide that I should get the Land Rover cleaned. The mud and manure are not right for North London. I drive to the local car jet-wash place where the nice Greek bloke walks slowly around my vehicle with total astonishment."My God! Where you been?!" I sigh.

"Wales. I've been in Wales. West… As far as you can go. "

As I wait for him and FOUR other Greeks to find my car under the allotment on wheels, Kelly calls me.

"OK, the insurance claim came through for the damaged footage. We can re-shoot the beach scenes on Barafundle Bay. When do you want to do it?"

"Um… "

June 3rd 2011

J.M. Barrie's 1904 play "...and straight on till morning for many days."

In the course of the current roll out of THIRD STAR I'm doing lots of Q and A's around the UK. I really like it. (I like Q's and I like A's – what's not to like?) The people who come to take part are, of course, film fans and so I have something in common with them already. On top of that – talking about the journey of this film with strangers, while I'm not one for counselling, is in some way cathartic.

One of the most asked questions though, is why the title or why the title had to change?

For a long time the film had the title "Barafundle Bay"... anyone who's seen the film will be able to work out why (unless they're dumber than the leader of the RMT). If you haven't it's because that is the (real-life) place that Benedict's character wants to see one last time with his best mates. It started as a working title and stuck.

Film investors want to know in advance that a professional who sells films – a 'Sales Agent'- thinks it 'might' make its money back. Our Sales Agent came on board very early and told me that the title had to change. This didn't bother me too much. I had always hoped that in a very wordy film a line or phrase would leap out at me. It never did.

Jump ahead three years and sure enough I have spent the entire time having to spell out the title to EVERYONE who we meet, phone, cast, and employ. For some reason people take a long time to get it even though it's phonetic.

Before I know it the shoot is over, the edit is drawing to a close and I still don't have a title. We're rapidly approaching picture-lock, the grade and our title designer needs to know what the film is called.

At this point of course there isn't just me, hiding in my study. All the parties who have joined the film are giving their opinion and we are now naming the film by committee! Some of the suggestions are so bad that I am ready to take my name off the film... "Forever Loved" was an all-time low.

Eventually, as I was actually researching something else, I saw an old illustration from Peter Pan and thought that Peter's instructions on how to get to Neverland might work. I like the fact that James would misquote things – hence Third star instead of Second – giving Miles the opportunity to say "Fuck. No wonder we're lost."

In J.M. Barrie's original tale (in the 1904 plays), Peter led Wendy and her brothers to Neverland by flying 'second to the right, and straight on till morning for many days', though it is stated in the novel (written later in 1911) that Peter made up these directions on the spot to impress Wendy. (This in fact struck me a very James thing to do.) Wendy and Peter then find the island only because it was out looking for them (the genius of Barrie).

In the 1953 Disney film, Peter Pan, the word 'star' is added to the directions Peter speaks: 'second star to the right, and straight on till morning.' That phrase is widely quoted, and was used again in the 1991 movie Hook. But the less said about Hook in a film blog the better.

The title THIRD STAR had arrived and was quickly signed off. The link to Peter Pan is inalienably British and subtly enforces the idea that these are Lost Boys and that in a way, James never will grow up.

I liked it, but I didn't love it. The two words in isolation made it a bit tougher and more 'boysy' – which was good. And the aim of a title that would travel all over the world was achieved – but it took a brilliant bit of design to bring it to life. Franki Goodwin, who designed the poster and titles, picked the perfect typeface but crucially added the simplest four pointed star as the dot of the 'i' and suddenly it felt like 'our film' again.

The link to the stars, and fate, and travel had long inspired this film and now we'd come full circle. So, that's the 'A' in more detail than I can usually give to the 'Q'...

But here's some other stuff I found out as some nice wider reading.

Did you know:

The third brightest star in the sky is Rigil Kentaurus, otherwise known as Alpha Centauri, which literally means foot of the centaur.

It's also known as Rigil Kent, Toliman, HR 5459 or the even catchier, HD 129620... (Anyone looking for unusual baby names may want to add that last one to the list.)

If you'd like to take a look, here's where it is... Right Ascension: 14 39 35.9 – Declination: -60 50 07 (Yep... right there.)

Although its 'Apparent Magnitude is -0.27' its 'Absolute Magnitude 4.4' (Hey – we all look different in the mirror.)

This beautiful astral body boasts the Spectral Type: G2V (...I KNOW!!!!!)

But our THIRD STAR... is also sometimes known as Proxima Centauri.

Why? Because it's the closest to us.

Yes. At a mere 4.3 light years... (not the brightest star – not the second brightest – but the third brightest star)... the THIRD STAR is the closest.

Take a look tonight. Raise a glass even, as many a traveller has since before we knew quite how we all hung together in this big bright universe. Good on you Alpha Centauri.

It is now November 25th 2011.

In between finishing a new script for the Western Edge slate I am sitting doing this Mug7 post. I have reached day 17 of the Third Star shoot diary – the Ferryman scenes. Just reading the call sheet takes me back to the highs and lows of that day in an instant.

The fact is that the film is out on DVD and the ferryman does not appear. It just didn't work in the final film for many reasons, so we cut it and only the ticket seller remains. The hours spent writing and re-writing the ferryman, the hours casting and filming are all on the cutting room floor.

The ferryman was in the script of 'Barafundle Bay' (you can read the scene in the script). He isn't in the film I made along with over a hundred other people – which became 'Third Star'. In a different reality what difference would this scene have made? Is the film better or worse?

I honestly don't know. But, what strikes me is that worrying about it is exactly what the ferryman was talking about.

"That's just life. Get on with it."

Instead of thinking about it I can choose to remember something else that happened that day.

Despite our cameras and equipment, the neon sign above the funny little shed and his eye makeup – a small group of ramblers, genuine members of the public hoping to go over to Ramsay Island, waited, patient and enthralled, while we finished a take and then gingerly stepped forward to buy a ticket from Karl. He duly obliged. Then they made their way to the boat...

I don't know what happened then. Did we pay them back? I hope so. But it was a bizarre and hilarious incident that is also absent from the film, but where, very briefly, it came alive for us thanks to Karl's performance.

Film making is great for encouraging the act of 'moving on'.

In writing, every scene should simply fulfil the need for the next to exist.

Every day shooting on set you have to be thinking in some part about the next. And every film is more experience towards making the next one better.

When problems nagged at me on set, I could watch the boys pushing the cart and it would strike me that life really does go in one direction. Better keep walking...

Wednesday March 7th 2012

"Having ideas is like having chessmen moving forward; they may be beaten, but they may start a winning game" Johann Wolfgang von Goethe

Some people have asked "why Mug 7?"

In setting up Western Edge Pictures (and producing Third Star) I wanted us to be as environmentally friendly as possible. I have always hated the waste on film sets. I think we are a particularly wasteful industry, because of the speed at which we have to produce our product. One tiny way to do this, and try and make a difference, was to ban polystyrene cups. You may think it's film stock, light and electricity that make films, but I'm fairly sure it's caffeine. Millions of cups a day – made one second before a cast or crewmember is called to do his duty and so discarded, or else drunk out of sheer boredom, the cup tossed away, and a fresh one taken to replace it. In over a decade on sets I never saw a polystyrene cup refilled.

In the week before shooting I sent the runners out into the locality to buy 50 mugs from charity shops. I told them to buy a few base-white mugs in each one. Spread the word that a local had come back to make a film, WITHOUT the money that Harry Potter and Robin Hood had had to throw at every problem… maybe they'll cut us some slack when we ask them to wait with a horde of other walkers while Benedict, JJ, Tom and Adam trudge past a seemingly empty vista.

Back at our production office in Stackpole, the runners painted numbers on them all, so each crewmember could choose a lucky number, or shape, or picture they liked. We took photos of them to archive our lovely crew with 'Mugshots'. One attempt at cutting our waste. And NO chance of our endless coffee cups blowing along the shore into baby dolphins… blow holes… anyway you get the picture. Did it work?..... No.

We were so rushed, so understaffed, and so busy. Caring for the mugs went by the wayside. Most ended up in unit base (still loved – but not on set) and recycled paper cups found their way on to the shoot. BUT – heartbroken though I was – many of the crew took their mugs home with their crew t-shirts. I learned what I needed to do next time to make this work, AND I have so many more ideas of how to make our film making credibly friendlier for the planet, whichever bit of it we're shooting in. We'd love to hear from anyone out there who has ideas to do that. If we can – we'll try them.

So – Mug 7, was mine. The 7th is my birthday. And there's a rather blurred photo of someone's much loved Jack Russell on the other side. I love making films, but it IS hard, and you have to be a bit of a terrier to try and get things done RIGHT. You just have to stay focused.

The Times Review By Kate Muir **** 26th June 2010

Third Star has a deceptively simple plot - three lads go camping with a dying friend - but it becomes both a mad romp along the stunning Pembrokeshire coast, and a heartbreaking insight into friendship. This British film from a new, woman director screens in the prestigious closing slot at the Edinburgh International Film Festival tonight.

Whether it is three men in a boat or four men in a tent, even pleasurable expeditions involve privations that bring out the best and worst in people, often amusingly. Hattie Dalton, the director, lets her cast of four josh and jape until their English middle-class reserve cracks beneath the comedy. Just because their mate is dying, the lads see no reason not to make fun of him, combining tenderness with brutal honesty. 'You look like s**t' says one, helpfully.

There is a knockout central performance by Benedict Cumberbatch as James, a strange, ethereal creature with a will of iron, who sports a brown fedora. James is 29 years old and will not see his thirtieth birthday because of an unspecified cancer. The old friends rounded up for his last hurrah are played by J.J. Feild, Adam Robertson and Tom Burke with a chemistry part-acted and partly brought about by the exigencies of the shoot - hours spent in frozen water in Barafundle Bay, in Pembrokeshire, coupled with grim food and collapsing tents. The wild Welsh landscape plays a role of its own, reflecting the men's mood and memories, all exquisitely shot on grainy film by Dalton in her first feature - she previously won a Bafta for a short film.

This is also a first for Vaughan Sivell, the scriptwriter, who catches the Hornbyesque nuances of bloke banter, and then probes deeper. All the characters are endearing in different ways - the dark side is provided offstage by death.

James, who is high on morphine, tries to lecture his friends on their futures as they stand on the thirtysomething cusp of commitments, families and careers that he will never have. The lads fight back with spliffs, beer and humour. 'It's like going for a walk with a sick, white Oprah,' they moan. Yet as they divest themselves of emotional and physical baggage - they are the most incompetent of campers - the men stuggle with an ethical dilemma, and prove themselves to be unlikely heroes. The camping trip slips into another dimension, and the surreal atmosphere is aided by looney cameos by fine actors - Hugh Bonneville as a beachcomber obsessed with toy lightsabres and Karl Johnson, a crusty old ferryman who, oddly, wears blue eyeshadow.

Third Star dares to tackle the taboo of too-early death with great humour and warmth. it is an assured debut for Dalton - and an economical one. with a budget of only £450,000 she has made a huge, sweeping film and her next move is worth watching.

I spent much of the latter half trying not to bawl out loud. yet the story's ending is uplifting as well as emotionally devastating, the audience sat in stunned silence afterwards.

Vaughan Sivell Biography

Vaughan Sivell is a Writer, Producer and CEO of Western Edge Pictures, he founded the company in 2008. His first feature film, *Third Star* which he wrote and produced, closed the Edinburgh Film Festival in 2010 and subsequently screened at festivals all over the world – reaching Seattle, Sydney, Sao Paolo and Taiwan to name but a few. It was released theatrically and on DVD in the UK and the US in 2011 – gathering a passionate following in the process.

Vaughan grew up in West Wales and had decided by the age of 10 that he was going to make films. He had an agent by 13 and 10 years of acting experience, including a classical theatre training, by the time he was 23.

The *Third Star* script was highly placed on the prestigious Britlist in 2008 and in 2010 was nominated for a BAFTA Cymru. The same year Vaughan produced his first play – the critically acclaimed *Eigengrau* which soon transferred to "Brits off Broadway" after its sell out run at the Bush Theatre.

Vaughan is a hands-on producer, writer and ambassador for Western Edge. Since *Third Star* Vaughan has focused on growing WEP's diverse slate and the establishment of source finance company Gennaker. *The Canal* - part funded by Gennaker - recently premiered at Tribeca. Vaughan is currently producing and directing feature documentary *Mr Calzaghe* and is set to direct drama feature *Bloodlines* later this year.